# PREFACE

This set of Guidelines has been produced by the National Agency for Finite Element Methods and Standards which is a section of the Stress Analysis Division within the National Engineering Laboratory run by the Secretary of State for Trade and Industry.

The Guidelines have been produced in the interests of users of Finite Element Methods with the intention of helping them to achieve high quality results. The document is a compendium of strategies, recommendations and advice. It can never be complete and rigid adherence to its provisions cannot guarantee valid analyses. It will be updated regularly in response to members' views and to technical changes in hardware and software.

Every care has been taken to ensure the accuracy of the statements made in the Guidelines but neither the Secretary of State nor the authors can accept any responsibility for errors and omissions in analyses using these Guidelines.

Further suggestions for improvement of the Guidelines will be carefully considered by the Steering Committee for inclusion in later editions. Such suggestions should be addressed to:

**W. M. Mair**
**National Agency for Finite Element Methods and Standards**
**National Engineering Laboratory**
**East Kilbride**
**Glasgow G75 0QU**
**Scotland**
**Telephone (03552) 20222 or (03552) 25688**

# CONTENTS

CONTENTS *(continued)*

CONTENTS *(continued)*

# GENERAL INTRODUCTION

## 0.1 PURPOSE AND LAYOUT OF MANUAL

This manual is produced by the UK National Agency for Finite Element Methods and Standards (NAFEMS) as a compendium of good practice; it is intended to be authoritative but has no formal regulatory status. Its aim is to guide users of finite element software and systems to achieve high quality results from analyses. Initially its scope is limited to the analysis of structures and directly related problems such as thermal conduction, kinematics and dynamics. It complements, but does not supplant, the user manuals which should form a part of all finite element systems.

The manual is laid out in seven working sections, plus a general introduction, as follows:

| Section | Title |
|---------|-------|
| 0 | General Introduction |
| 1 | Analysis Specification |
| 2 | Method Validation |
| 3 | Modelling and Formulation |
| 4 | Analysis Execution |
| 5 | Results Interpretation |
| 6 | Documentation |
| 7 | Analysis System Expectations |

Section 1 begins with a specimen pro forma for an analysis specification, which is explained in the subsequent text. Sections 3 and 5 begin with check lists for use by analysis planners and supervisors, again amplified in the text.

Each section is organised using structured numbers so that additions and alterations can be made with minimum disruption.

Each sheet has an issue date which is the sole means of identification of revisions.

## 0.2  FINITE ELEMENT STRUCTURAL ANALYSIS — BRIEF SUMMARY

Finite element analysis is essentially an *approximate method* for calculating the behaviour of a real structure by performing an algebraic solution of a set of equations describing an *idealised model structure* with a finite number of variables. In this model the real structure is represented by a set of elements bounded by a mesh or grid of lines and surfaces. Each element is assumed to be defined by its boundary geometry, its material properties and a few basic parameters such as thickness and cross-section area. Its behaviour in relation to adjoining elements is assumed to be fully described by its boundary loads and displacements which in turn are assumed to be functions of a finite number of discrete variables, nominally defined at the nodes of the geometrical mesh or convenient points on the boundaries. The behaviour of the complete, idealised structure is determined as the aggregate behaviour of its elements.

The basic equations of equilibrium, compatibility and state are set up and solved in terms of the discrete boundary variables and the behaviour within elements is then derived from the values calculated at their boundaries.

Thus any finite element analysis is only as good as:

- the model of the structure (ie the geometric mesh and the elements within it)

- the assumptions embedded in the properties used for each element

- the representation of the external loads and constraints in terms of the discrete boundary variables.

Note that the solution of the structural equations is often exact within the numerical accuracy of computing. The important assumptions within the method (and hence the intrinsic limitations in accuracy) are at individual element scale.

Therefore, this manual concentrates mainly upon the choice of a suitable model (grid geometry and element selection) the controlled preparation of data and the interpretation of results at element scale.

The mathematics of problem solution and the choice of solution methods are only touched upon and these more in the context of economic and feasible solutions than reliability of results.

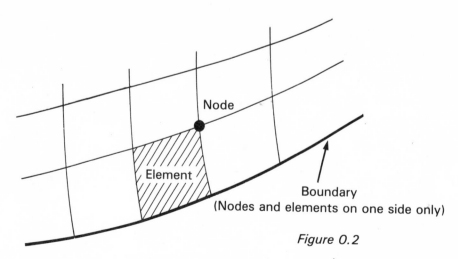

*Figure 0.2*

## 0.3  PLANNING THE ANALYSIS

Before commencing any substantial analysis the user should prepare an outline plan relating the objectives of the analysis to the facilities, resources and time-scale at his disposal.

Aspects of the plan which may be relevant are related to the following key issues.

| Aspect | Resources | | Elapsed time | Other requirements |
|---|---|---|---|---|
| | Man hours | Cost | | |
| Familiarisation<br>— with methods<br>— with facilities | ✓ | | ✓ | Consultation? |
| Data acquisition<br>— Structure, properties<br>— Loads, constraints<br>— Interfaces | ✓ | ✓ | ✓ | Someone else's work schedule? |
| Understanding of problem<br>— Results required<br>— Level of detail | ✓ | | ✓ | Preliminary analysis required? |
| Problem formulation<br>— Data preparation<br>— Data entry<br>— Validation/debugging | ✓ | ✓ | ✓ | Preprocessor facilities? |
| Execution<br>— Computer run(s)<br>— Output presentation | | ✓ | ✓ | Facility availability? |
| Interpretation<br>— Engineering Assessment<br>— Real structure behaviour | ✓ | ✓ | ✓ | Postprocessor facilities? |

## 0.4 RESOURCING AND AUTHORISATION

In general the analyst will be faced with one of two situations:

**(a)** an instruction to perform the analysis (presupposing supervisor's awareness of probable cost/elapsed time),

**(b)** a request for an analysis subject to cost or time-scale constraints.

In both cases the analyst should ensure that sufficient resources will be available at the right time to complete the task.

In case **(a)** this may mean fitting in with other peoples' work schedules and facility access times or conflict with other tasks for the analyst himself. The supervisor should always be made aware of implications before the job starts; perform a feasibility study, if in doubt.

In case **(b)** the need for resource confirmation and authorisation is obvious.

**NB:** A job stopped for inadequate resources is a waste of time and money.

## 0.5  ACCREDITED USERS AND EXPERTS

Finite element analysis is a powerful and efficient tool in competent hands.

If safety depends on the results of the analysis it must be performed, supervised or verified by an engineer of adequate experience and status.

As yet there are no laid down standards for accrediting users; the following guidelines should be followed.

- The analyst and/or supervisor should be educated to at least first degree standard in a relevant scientific discipline (engineering, physics, mathematics, computing etc).

- The analyst and/or supervisor should be trained in problem modelling and use of the finite element tools at their disposal, to the satisfaction of a supervisor or chartered engineer or equivalent status.

- Training should either be formal, via reputable instruction course(s), informal on-the-job via competent supervision or by reference to approved manuals and training aids.

- In the latter instance there should always be a fall back to an experienced and reputable expert for consultation.

- The supervisor or analyst should be capable of, and in all instances should conduct, an appraisal of analysis results based on physical appreciation and experience of related problems.

*Incompetent analysis gives results which are, at best, unreliable and, at worst, positively misleading.*

Throughout this document the following definitions are implied:

An *expert analyst either* has prior experience which makes him an accredited user as described above *or* has adequate professional training plus the ability, time and resources for familiarisation or research in relevant facets of the method.

An *expert consultant* has extensive prior experience and high professional standing in understanding and applying the analysis system to relevant practical problems. It is important to establish the credentials of self-proclaimed experts (eg in consultants' bureaux), if possible by reference to the originators of the system.

An *expert supervisor* combines the normal qualifications for professional supervision with prior experience in the direction of similar analyses and/or expertise in the principles and practice of finite element analysis. The supervisor's essential functions are to provide informed engineering guidance and critique of all aspects of a job specification and direction about results interpretation.

## 1. ANALYSIS SPECIFICATION

Finite element analysis is one important step in a design or validation process.

A *clear statement* of intent is helpful to the analyst himself and indispensible to a second party who will execute, use or contribute to the analysis.

This is best embodied in a formal specification. Therefore

**A formal specification, based on the guidelines of this section should be prepared for any analysis of significance.**

To aid the preparation of a specification, a pro forma is provided on the following pages. Using this format, Section 1.0-2 contains the job control information including a box for recording the authority (directive or charge number) against which the job is to be performed. Other headings are self-explanatory or are amplified subsequently.

Sections 1.0-2 and 1.0-3 are essential information which will always be required. Section 1.0-4 is optional, to be used if necessary.

Continuation sheets should be inserted for additional entries for which space is inadequate.

Separate Section 1.0-3 sheets may be used for each combination of loading and boundary conditions, if appropriate.

JOB NAME: ...................................................... Job No ..............

Prepared by ...................................................... Date ................

Approved by ...................................................... Authority.............

1. PROBLEM DESCRIPTION

Ref. Drawing No ...........
Sketches attached ...........

*Structure*

*Nature of Problem*

*Loading Conditions*

2. ANALYSIS REPRESENTATION

Ref. Sketches ..............

Grid

Element Selection

Special Features

Symmetry and Boundary Conditions

Loading Actions

Non-linear Representation

JOB NAME: . . . . . . . . . . . . . . . . . . . . . . . . . . . . . . . . . . . . . . . . . . .    Job No . . . . . . . . . . . . . .

3.  OUTPUT — REQUIRED

Loading case(s) . . . . . . . . . . . . . . . . . . . . . . . . . . . . . . . . . . . . . . . . . . . . . . . . . . . . . . . . . .

Boundary/symmetry conditions . . . . . . . . . . . . . . . . . . . . . . . . . . . . . . . . . . . . . . . . . . . . . . .

*Results, Selection and Presentation (Ref. P 1.3)*

*Diagnostic Output*

JOB NAME: . . . . . . . . . . . . . . . . . . . . . . . . . . . . . . . . . . . . . . . . . . . . . . . . . Job No . . . . . . . . . . . . . .

## 4. SOLUTION METHODS

Analysis system(s) . . . . . . . . . . . . . . . . . . . . . . . . . . . . . . . . . . . . . . . . . . . . . . . . . . . . . . . . . . . . . . . .

Static analysis . . . . . . . . . . . . . . . . . . . . . . . . . . . . . . . . . . . . . . . . . . . . . . . . . . . . . . . . . . . . . . . . . . . .

Dynamic analysis . . . . . . . . . . . . . . . . . . . . . . . . . . . . . . . . . . . . . . . . . . . . . . . . . . . . . . . . . . . . . . . . .

| | Identifier | Standard |
|---|---|---|
| **5. RELATED ANALYSES**<br><br>*Adjoining Structures*<br><br><br><br>Interaction responsibility . . . . . . . . . . . . . . . . . . . . . . . . . . . | | |
| *Other Analyses* | Person responsible | |

## 6. RELATED TESTS

*Basic Data Tests*

| Test specimen type | Ref. No | Basic data required |
|---|---|---|
| | | |

*Supporting Tests*

## 1.1 PHYSICAL PROBLEM DESCRIPTION

It is always good practice to begin by showing drawings or sketches illustrating the problem to be solved.

The analyst should then summarise the pertinent characteristics of the problem to be solved, using the following as a guide.

### 1.1.1 *The Structure or Region of Structure to be Analysed*

- Basic geometry
- Material and construction/lay-up used
- Joints and special structural features
- Adjoining structure and/or supports or foundations
- Boundary conditions
- Purpose of analysis
- Sources of authentic data.

### 1.1.2 *Nature of Problem to be Solved*

- Linear or non-linear static stress/displacement analysis
- Flexibility analysis
- Modal frequency/response analysis
- Quasi-linear or non-linear dynamic response
- Impact or stress-wave analysis
- Thermal conduction and/or thermal stress analysis
- Nature of results and/or special solution requirements.

### 1.1.3 *Nature of the External Actions — Sources of Authentic Data*

- Imposed displacements, including contact conditions
- Loading systems, eg fixed or 'follower' forces

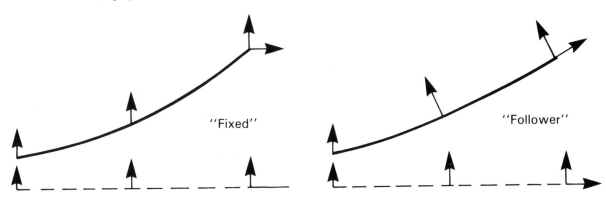

**Forces on Deformed Structure**

*Figure 1.1.3a*

- Special generalised forces or displacements

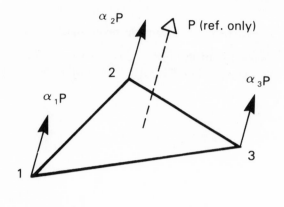

$$U = \alpha_1 U_1 + \alpha_2 U_2 + \alpha_3 U_3$$

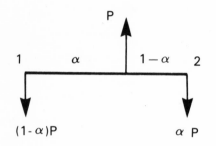

$$U = U^+ - U^-$$

$$U = U_\alpha - (1-\alpha)U_1 - \alpha U_2$$

$$U = 1/l \int_0^L U(x)dx - \frac{U_1 + U_2}{2}$$

**Generalised Forces
(Examples)**

**Displacements**

*Figure 1.1.3b*

- Body forces, inertias etc
- Environmental conditions.

## 1.2 ANALYSIS REPRESENTATION

This section deals with the statement of the analyst's intentions for representing the physical problem. Further details concerning problem modelling are given in Section 3.

Pertinent features of the analysis, supported by brief justification, should be defined using the following as a guide.

### 1.2.1 *Analysis Grid (Normally Provide Diagram(s))*

- Rules/algorithms for subdividing continuous regions
- Boundary approximations (eg piecewise linear)
- Node sequencing requirements
- Substructuring requirements and interface definition
- Mesh generation aids to be used.

### 1.2.2 *Element Selection*

- Element types assigned to particular structural regions
- General or special elements required
- Modelling aids to be used.

### 1.2.3 *Sub-scale Features*

The analyst will often be faced with detailed physical features whose scale is too small to be represented explicitly, eg the layers in a laminated composite, machining details, joints etc.

In some cases these only have a very local effect (eg stress raisers) but in others they significantly affect the structural behaviour in their neighbourhood.

The method of allowance for such features (often very important in relation to the accuracy of results) must be clearly defined, using diagrams where appropriate.

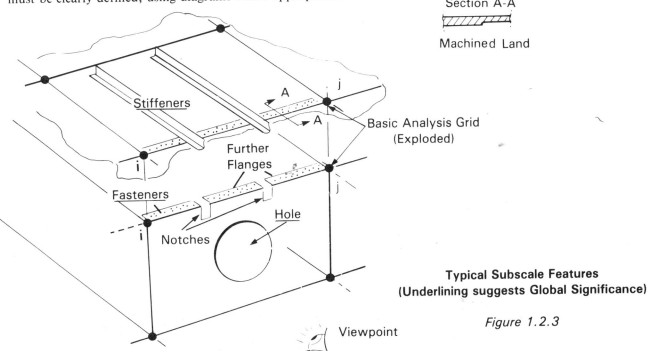

**Typical Subscale Features**
**(Underlining suggests Global Significance)**

*Figure 1.2.3*

1.2.4 *Symmetry and Boundary Conditions (Use Diagrams)*

- Proposed axes/planes of symmetry
- Representation of determinate boundary conditions
- Treatment of indeterminate conditions (eg contact problems).

1.2.5 *Loading Actions*

- Discrete parameter representations of continuous boundary loads
- Body forces and inertias
- Representation of environmental conditions (eg temperature)
- Representations of stochastic loadings.

1.2.6 *Non-linear Representation*

- Finite, small deflection; geometric stiffness
- Large deformation
- Material non-linearities, viscoelasticity etc
- Bifurcation, post-buckling.

## 1.3    RESULTS AND DIAGNOSTICS

The analyst must specify clearly what results are required, how they are to be selected and presented and what checks or diagnostic aids are required to validate them.                    August 1984

Results required must be clearly identified with loading cases and boundary conditions.

### 1.3.1    *Type of Results*

- Deflections, strains, forces, stresses, temperature etc

- Maximum stresses, strains, deflections *or* collapse load (limit analysis) *or* creep rupture load

- Global properties (stiffnesses, flexibilities etc)

- Eigenvalues/vectors

- Frequency response functions

- Time histories of displacement, velocity, acceleration etc.

- Special results (eg energy densities for optimisation).

### 1.3.2    *Selection*

- Points, sections, regions for tabulation

- Selection by cases

- Selection by comparative criteria

- Selection to suit codes or data sheets

- Requirements for user interaction

- Interpolation and extrapolation

- Post-processor aids to be used.

### 1.3.3    *Presentation*

- Text display and tabulation

- Direct point-by-point/element-by-element plots

- Time history plots

- Section and carpet plots  }  two-tone or colour

- Contour plots

- Interactive graphic displays

- Bar — or pie — chart plots

- Animated displays

- Special presentations (describe)

- Presentation aids/systems to be used.

### 1.3.4 *Diagnostics*

- In-built checks required

- Special checks and criteria

- Error/accuracy messages required

- Special outputs for user assessment

- Diagnostic aids to be used.

## 1.4 SOLUTION METHODS

For many straightforward, eg linear static, analyses, there may be no alternative methods available and hence no need for specification. However, in more complex cases, especially in dynamics, there may be choices for the analyst as set out below. Further details and criteria for selection are considered in Section 4.

### 1.4.1 *Analysis System*

Specify the system(s) to be used to handle:

- Static analysis

- Dynamic analysis/impact analysis

- Thermal/thermostructural analysis

- Special non-linear analysis.

### 1.4.2 *Static Analysis*

- Force or displacement formulation/solution

- Elimination, factorisation or front solution

- Non-linear solution technique

- Eigen solution method (elastic stability).

### 1.4.3 *Dynamic Analysis*

- Direct or modal response

- Eigen solution method (or statement of criteria)

- Steady state or transient, quasi-static or wave solution

- Deterministic response technique or criteria

- Stochastic response technique or criteria.

## 1.5   RELATED ANALYSIS

A structural or thermal analysis is often conducted in conjunction with, or in support of, one or more other analyses.

It is important to record from the outset any interdependencies with other analyses.

### 1.5.1   *Adjoining Structures*

- Identification of neighbouring analysis and data standard

- Definition of geometric, loading and kinematic boundary conditions

- Requirements for results to or from adjoining structures

- Responsibility for interaction calculation.

### 1.5.2   *Related Structural/Design Analyses*

(For example optimisation, fatigue life, local stress analysis etc)

- Identification and data standard

- Inputs required from related analysis, with dates

- Outputs required for related analysis, with dates

- Feedback and iterative solution requirements

- Name(s) of responsible person(s).

### 1.5.3   *Related Non-structural Analyses*

(For example aerodynamic loading, control system etc)

As above plus:

- Responsibility for data/model matching

- Acceptance criteria (from recipient to supplier of data).

## 1.6 RELATED EXPERIMENTS

A finite element analysis may depend, for some of its data, or may be supported by structural/thermal tests. Any such conditions should be recorded at the outset.

### 1.6.1 *Dependence on Test Data*

This situation must be handled with extreme care and in all but the simplest cases, *should not be tackled without expert advice.*

Test data will always contain experimental errors which, in many cases, imply inconsistency with the assumptions embedded in finite element analysis methods. This is especially true if redundant data (eg all the elements of a stiffness or flexibility matrix) are determined independently by test. The following principles should be applied.

- Use test data, wherever possible, to determine 'natural' stiffness, inertia or flexibility values, ie properties expressed in terms of the minimum number of fundamental physical variables (eg bar stiffness expressed in terms of stress/strain or *relative* end displacement).

- Use any redundant test data to smooth the natural properties by standard error-reduction methods.

- Expand 'natural' data to conventional stiffness, inertia of flexibility formats using geometric data identical to that used in the finite element model.

- In extremis, use simple devices such as taking the mean of a matrix and its transpose to ensure symmetry when that is physically demanded and/or adjusting principal diagonal terms to establish equilibrium or compatibility to as many figures as are significant in the analysis.

### 1.6.2 *Analysis Confirmed by Test*

Requirements here are less demanding but the analyst should try to ensure that the following match as nearly as possible, between analysis and experiment:

- Physical geometry (especially tolerances)

- Loading cases and loading distributions

- Support and constraint conditions

- Adjoining structure/rig

- Material properties and/or environmental conditions

- Measurement/calculation location points.

## 2. METHOD VALIDATION

The basic theory and the application software used for any finite element analysis must be adequate to represent the problem, numerically accurate and robust in dealing with the many variations and singular features found in typical usage.

A separate manual gives details of fundamental and practical tests which can be used for validation and these notes are limited to general guidance. Before commencing any significant analysis the analyst and/or supervisor should satisfy themselves that:

- The basic theory is sound and applicable to the particular problem

- The methods/software have satisfied certain fundamental tests for soundness and convergence

- Benchmark tests have been performed to demonstrate satisfactory performance

- In special circumstances, specific tests have demonstrated performance in similar circumstances to the proposed analysis.

## 2.1    BASIC THEORY

The analyst/supervisor should ensure that the system manuals or supporting documentation and references provide adequate justification of the soundness of basic theory.

Since numerical approximations are often buried deeply within the theory (especially the reliance on approximate area and volume integration) it is often difficult to establish integrity on a definitive, analytical basis.

**A finite element analysis system should be used in significant safety calculations only if it is supported by adequate descriptions of:**

- **the theories used in element formulation and problem solution**

- **the assumptions and limitations inherent in its modelling.**

## 2.2 FUNDAMENTAL TESTS

Where complete analytical demonstration of integrity is infeasible, analysis systems should be shown to satisfy a number of fundamental tests.

A first rate system will contain such justification within its own documentation, presented with clarity and conviction.

If documentation does not exist, the analysis system should be used with caution unless and until such tests are performed to the user's satisfaction.

Some specific tests are listed below.

- Invariance of element stiffness/flexibility matrices with choice of local reference axes.

- Absence of internal stress under rigid body motions.

- Freedom from spurious 'kinematic modes' ie special combinations of distortional displacements yielding zero stresses.

- Convergence to exact solutions in special cases, where available.

- 'Patch test' for constant stress fields, invariant with choice of local element boundaries.

In certain cases, analysis may fail some of the above tests but still perform satisfactorily in specific applications. Specialist advice or adequate justifying documentation should always be available before placing reliance on 'doubtful' formulations.

## 2.3 BENCHMARK TESTS

Benchmark tests serve many useful purposes, eg demonstrations of performance and accuracy of basic theory and problem formulation facilities, indications of cost/time performance on specific computing hardware, familiarisation of users with the system, its input/output and operational features.

NAFEMS is sponsoring a collection of benchmark tests covering all the major applications of finite element structural analysis and all the common element types and arrangements.

Analysis systems suppliers will be encouraged to present results for all appropriate benchmark tests and failure to do so will be seen as an adverse factor in system selection.

Until benchmark standards are widely accepted, analysts should seek appropriate tests and assure themselves that these have been performed to their satisfaction.

Performance in accepted tests should be recorded or referenced as part of the job specification.

## 2.4    SPECIFIC DEMONSTRATIONS

Where major safety considerations arise or where unusual applications of a method are involved, it is advisable to seek specific confirmation of the method validity or accuracy.

This means relating the subject problem to a reference analysis which is *either* similar but simpler and backed by exact analytical or an established semi-analytical solution *or* is similar in nature and complexity and backed by experimental evidence.

In novel applications it is good practice to devise a specific and closely related experiment and perform a reference analysis for the express purpose of method confirmation.

It is also good practice, before embarking on any complex analysis to carry out a coarse-mesh or grossly simplified analysis first (see Section 3), in order to:

- gain experience in the use of all facilities employed

- identify the critical regions of structure and scale of idealisation needed

- help in the selection of results.

## 3.  MODELLING AND FORMULATION

Selection and preparation of the finite element model can have more bearing on the accuracy of results than choice of the basic methods and tools to be used.

The analyst must understand the tools being used and must be accurate and consistent in preparing data.

Automatic data checking facilities should be used as far as possible to verify that data are logically correct, physcially meaningful and what the analyst intended.

*Good modelling practice*

- Always try to make the finite element model represent all potentially effective material in the problem area.

- Traditional (force/stress based) modelling practice was to simplify structures by assuming load paths and neglecting 'secondary', structural material. In finite element analysis this practice is usually unnecessary and always misleading. It should be reserved only for supplementary analysis where some structural material or connections may be considered unreliable.

- Remember Saint-Venant's principle and concentrate modelling detail in the regions of most structural concern. Use coarse-mesh analysis to help define these regions.

- When two or more complex structural regions intersect over a relatively small common boundary use substructuring for economy in analysis and ease of definition.

- Subdivide complex structures into identifiable zones for modelling and checking purposes, even if not using substructuring for solution.

The following check list and specific guidelines are intended to help the analyst to maintain control of the modelling and data preparation processes and not to provide a manual of techniques.

## 3.0.1  *Basic Geometry*

Note the source and standard of all geometric data.

### 3.0.1.1  Bounding lines and surfaces

State clearly whether bounding lines/surfaces represent:

- outer/inner boundaries
- centre lines/surfaces
- structural neutral axes/surfaces
- other convenient data.

Ensure the following are adequately represented:

- line/surface continuity or steps/offsets
- local slope magnitude and continuity
- local curvatures.

If points or lines are used to define lines/surfaces, ensure that:

- interpolation rules/formulae are specified
- these are consistent with those implied in the analysis system.

### 3.0.1.2  Mesh selection

A mesh should be selected to satisfy certain criteria. Note which of the following apply, and in what priority sequence:

- Key lines follow — principal structural members
  — thickness/property changes boundaries
  —principal stress directions, isostatics or other preferred directions
- Mesh regularity between key lines
- Maintenance of acceptable element proportions
- Mesh continuity
- Mesh density and local shape near major stress raisers
- Matching associated analyses
- Ease of interpolation, section plotting, extrapolation etc
- Other specified criteria.

Note: The mesh should always cover or represent all actual structure whether considered 'primary' or 'secondary'.

### 3.0.1.3 Special features

Identify clearly, as appropriate:

- boundaries with adjoining structures

- axes or planes of symmetry

- external and internal constraint points

- location of releases (hinges, slides etc).

### 3.0.1.4 Facilities to be used

Identify and specify appropriate parameters for:

- mesh generation aids

- geometry display* (nature, views, sections etc)

- special geometry generation aids (eg consistent substructure geometry, axis transformations etc).

*Note: Automatic plots from actual computer input data should be mandatory for all significant analyses.

### 3.0.2 *Structural Elements*

### 3.0.2.1 Element selection

Base the choice of elements upon:

- adequate representation of problem geometry

- representation of relevant structural behaviour

- proven performance in similar problems

- adequate coverage of expected stress gradients or similar state variations

- number and position of stress output points

- understanding and usefulness of results.

3.0.2.2 Element property idealisation

Ensure that the following are adequately represented:

- inclusion of all potentially effective structure

- effects of offsets of neutral axes/surfaces from datum lines

- allowances for finite thickness/depth effects

- major joints as flexible elements in their own right

- sub-scale joints and perforations within elements

- other sub-scale features (reinforcements, swages, pocketing etc)

- allowances for non-ideal member intersections (eg offset flanges, cleats etc)

- material properties throughout the expected load/environment range.

3.0.2.3 Special elements

NB: Not to be used without adequate expertise and/or professional support.

When used, ensure that:

- element property matrices are fundamentally consistent (static equilibrium etc) to the internal computing accuracy of the systems

- element geometry is consistent with basic structure geometry to the same accuracy

- elements are compatible with adjoining structure (boundary continuity, removal of singularities etc).

3.0.2.4 Facilities to be used

Specify with appropriate parameters:

- mesh generation aids

- logic, connectivity, consistency checks

- displays of element data in context.

### 3.0.2.5 Data vetting

Whether special facilities are available or not, check data as input to the computer to ensure that:

- all elements are specified, in correct location

- nodal connections are correct

- property values are sensible/continuous.

### 3.0.3 *External Actions*

### 3.0.3.1 External and body forces

Note the source and standard of all loading data.

Ensure that data are supplied or transformed to match the structural analysis mesh; then ensure that:

- All external loads (plus constraint forces) are in equilibrium, globally and have correct local resultants.

- All loading cases, built up from external actions and body forces to equilibrate them, are complete and fully specified.

- All loading cases are matched to appropriate boundary conditions (eg symmetric or antisymmetric).

- Load interpolation/distribution formulae (implied in loading data) can be reconciled with element boundary assumptions.

- Inertia data are consistent with structure geometry.

### 3.0.3.2 Imposed displacements

If displacements are imposed, particular care is needed to ensure that they are kinematically sensible.

Check for absence of large relative local deformations.

If a contact problem is to be solved ensure that:

     *either* explicit facilities are available

     *or* there is adequate analyst expertise.

3.0.4 *Constraints*

3.0.4.1 External (single-point) constraints

External constraints must be:

- kinematically sufficient (ie all relevant rigid body freedoms are suppressed)

- physically reasonable

- consistent with the appropriate loading cases and especially with the presence of thermal strains.

It may be necessary to use single-point constraint facilities to eliminate spurious degrees of freedom (eg normal to unsupported nodes in structures built up from membrane elements).

3.0.4.2 Multi-point constraints

Attention must be given to:

- the need for multi-point constraints

- their accuracy of specification.

Multi-point constraints may be needed in the following circumstances:

- to simulate rigid connection of points for whatever purpose

- to deal with offset loading, attachments or supports

- to generate standard types of boundary conditions (eg plane sections remain plane and undistorted)

- to correct for geometric mismatch between adjoining elements or substructures

- to introduce local mesh subdivision

- to handle nodal releases (hinges, slides etc)

- to reduce matrix ill-conditioning by coupling degrees of freedom.

Multi-point constraints are normally introduced in one of two ways:

**(a)** By writing explicit equations connecting relevant degrees of freedom.

**(b)** By defining a displacement transformation (which in effect applies the solution of the constraint equations).

In either case the coefficients concerned must be:

- consistent among themselves

- consistent with structure geometry

} to the accuracy of internal working in the analysis system.

This is best achieved by accurate computation direct from nodal geometry.

### 3.0.5 *Adjacent Structures and Symmetry*

Where a structure terminates in a boundary with another structure one of four conditions commonly arises:

**(a)** passive adjoining structure (ie not itself separately loaded),

**(b)** active, dissimilar structure (self-loaded),

**(c)** symmetry (reflective, skew, radial etc),

**(d)** repetition of identical structure.

These cases must be treated as follows:

**(i)** Passive structure is represented by a special stiffness matrix using common boundary geometry (see Section 3.0.2.3).

**(ii)** Dissimilar structure, separately analysed. Ensure consistency and completeness of:

- geometry (to system internal working accuracy)

- interface analysis definition or assumptions

- loading cases, for both parties

- kinematic constraints for all cases.

(iii) Symmetric boundary conditions are normally introduced as single-point constraints (see Section 3.0.4.1).

These must be consistent with loading cases.

(iv) Repetition of identical structure

- most systems use simple multi-point constraints (Section 3.0.4.2)

- coefficients are normally unity, therefore exact

- ensure accurate one-to-one assignment.

## 3.1    GEOMETRY

Nodal geometry is the most readily controlled of all data.

Many mesh generators exist for subdividing continuous regions of structure or for repeating topological patterns; their use is highly recommended.

All depend on accurate specification of a number of control lines or surfaces which define the real structure. These must themselves be accurately defined and checked.

**In general the best checks for geometry are graphical displays. Every significant analysis should use plots or screen displays for checking line and surface shape and continuity and element connectivity. Machine — generated plots should be annexed to the specification, Section 2.**

Numerical accuracy of nodal geometry is important only up to a limited number of significant figures, usually compatible with the discrimination of the human eye.

*BUT*

**If ever coincident points are separately specified (eg connections between substructures or constraints) their coordinates must be *identical* to as many figures as are significant in analysis; this may mean 10-16 figures). This requirement is particularly severe if two different frames of reference are used.**

*IN GENERAL,* **if coincident nodes are specified, use one member of each pair as master and derive the coordinates of others from them, to the order of precision used in analysis.**

**The same principle must apply when special element stiffnesses are introduced.**

An important consideration can be finite thickness of structural members in relation to their separation. Most line, plate and shell elements are defined as though infinitesimally thin and their properties are normally defined relative to their centre lines or principal axes.

**PLATE SECTION**

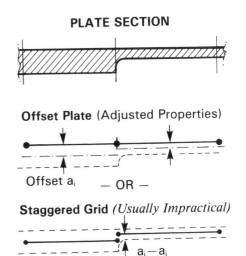

**Offset Plate** (Adjusted Properties)

Offset $a_i$    — OR —

**Staggered Grid** *(Usually Impractical)*

$a_i - a_j$

**Finite Thickness Effects**

*Figure 3.1*

When these effects are significant, lines and surfaces must either be defined in neutral planes (which may mean offsets at adjacent elements which must be specifically accounted for) or elements must be idealised to correct their properties.

The nodal geometry defines element shape and this may have a significant bearing on the accuracy of the analysis.

An essential part of element checking, often built into the analysis system, is avoidance of shapes outside recommended limits. Such checks must always be followed back to the basic geometry and may cause substantial changes in grid patterns.

## 3.2   ELEMENT SELECTION AND IDEALISATION

### 3.2.1  *General*

The analyst must carefully select the types of element best suited to the solution of the particular problem in hand and must then specify element properties (section dimensions, materials etc) which faithfully represent the real structure. Particular care must be taken (consulting the manuals) in deciding between membrane and flexural plate elements, faceted or curved shell elements and in selecting and using special (eg singular crack tip) elements.

Only in the simplest cases (eg continuous shells or solids) is the choice of properties obvious and necessarily accurate. The following is à selection of typical situations confronting the analyst which affect idealisation.

- Simplification of boundaries (complex curves replaced by straight lines, parabolae, conics, cubics) affects also the load idealisation.

- Structural joints and perforations below analysis scale — these must be allowed for either explicitly as elements in their own right (eg linear/non-linear springs for bolted joints) or by modifying the effective material properties of elements (a useful treatment for mechanically fastened or lightened shear webs etc).

- Finite thickness effects affecting (for example) flexural and torsional properties of beam, tube and box-type structures (see also Section 3.1) and introducing local offsets.

- Laminated construction where individual layers are combined into one set of plate or shell properties.

- Locally reinforced skins with stiffeners closer in pitch than element scale (remember that orthotropic membrane and flexural properties must be simulated as well as correct neutral plane position). This is a combined geometry and element property idealisation.

- Material properties, often non-linear and/or time (or strain rate) dependent, are usually simplified to linear or piecewise-linear equivalents.

- Actual structures often (for reasons of physical clearance etc) do not intersect cleanly at common points. Idealised elements are often used which assume locally simplified boundaries and common connection points. These geometrical inaccuracies must be recognised and allowed for when interpreting the analysis results. In particular, allowance must be made for the effects of features such as offset attachment flanges, cleated joints etc on stiffness, thermal conductivity etc.

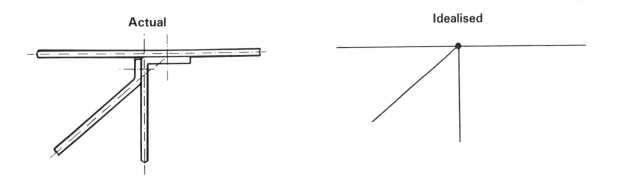

**Actual**     **Idealised**

*Figure 3.2.1*   **Imperfect Intersection**

### 3.2.2  *Data Checking*

Element data can be checked automatically for consistency and logic (eg topology) but actual property values can only be scrutinised for the more violent aberrations.

A good analysis system may check some or all of the following:

- Type consistency (correct number of nodes, properties etc).

- Nodal connectivity (geometrical adjacency and sequence).

- Shape limitations (see Section 3.1).

- Elements omitted or duplicated.

- Continuity of properties (only approximate).

- Element compatibility (node commonality, singularity removal, etc).

As with nodal geometry, good visual display is often the best method of checking.

**Where facilities exist, the analyst should display:**

- **element locations and types relative to the grid**

- **element section properties (section, carpet or contour plots)**

- **material types or key properties**

- **special data such as layer orientations (fibre composites).**

### 3.2.3  *Special Elements*

Sometimes the analyst needs to introduce special elements to supplement those available in the system. This requires extreme care, especially if element data are derived from tests (see Section 1.6). Element data must satisfy the basic requirements of Sections 2.1 and 2.2.

**In particular, element stiffnesses and related properties must be geometrically and statically consistent to the order of accuracy associated with solution precision.**

Likewise the element geometry, at all points of connection to the main structure must be consistent with the basic geometry to the same accuracy.


IN GENERAL, special elements should not be introduced except under the close supervision of an expert analyst.

## 3.3  EXTERNAL ACTIONS (FORCES AND DISPLACEMENTS)

### 3.3.1  *Loads*

Loading actions and environmental conditions are often defined by analysis or experiment outside the control of the finite element analysis. It is important that data so supplied should be consistent, especially, with the geometry of the structure.

**Always record the source and standard of externally supplied data and demonstrate geometrical compatibility with the structure.**

The most important aspects of controlling loading data are the same as for all structural analyses. Basically, external loads, together with any external constraint forces must be in equilibrium. If externally derived loads are transformed to match the structural grid, equilibrium must be established in the transformed condition.

In many instances (eg aircraft in flight), loading systems comprise external actions equilibrated by body forces which may themselves be treated, for analysis purposes, as external loading actions.

In this case it is common practice to build up loading cases from unbalanced external actions and simplified systems of body forces to restore global (and often local) equilibrium.

**Always ensure that loading cases, compounded from unbalanced sets of forces, are in overall equilibrium and give the correct local load resultant (eg shear force and bending moment) to the order of accuracy expected of the analysis.**

It is fundamental to finite element analysis that continuously varying loads are defined in terms of a finite number of parameters. It is important that the parametric definition of external loading actions be compatible with the corresponding element and interelement boundary loading conditions used in the basic theory. Provided that compatibility is established at nodal grid scale any residual differences (locally self-equilibrating by definition) can usually be satisfactorily resolved by local analysis and superposition (Saint-Venant's principle) (see Fig. 3.3.1).

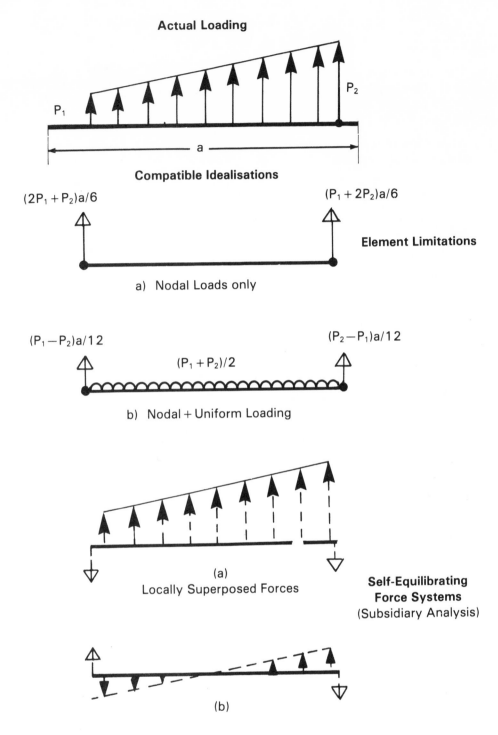

**Actual Loading**

**Compatible Idealisations**

$(2P_1 + P_2)a/6$       $(P_1 + 2P_2)a/6$

**Element Limitations**

a) Nodal Loads only

$(P_1 - P_2)a/12$    $(P_1 + P_2)/2$    $(P_2 - P_1)a/12$

b) Nodal + Uniform Loading

(a)
Locally Superposed Forces

**Self-Equilibrating
Force Systems**
(Subsidiary Analysis)

(b)

**Load System Compatibility**

*Figure 3.3.1*

### 3.3.2 *Structural Temperatures*

Varying structural temperatures give rise to significant internal strains and stresses in many structures.

It is important to establish that the analysis system can properly take account of these effects; considerable care is often needed in introducing thermal (or any other) internal strains.

Assuming that adequate facilities exist, there are no adequate means of checking temperature data other than indications of gross discontinuities.

Data may be derived from a parallel analysis using the same basic geometry, in which case graphical display may already be used to give confidence in the results. In any event, a temperature contour plot, or zonal shading plot, is an excellent visual aid to confirm data validity.

### 3.3.3 *Displacements*

Imposed displacements are not often encountered, but when they are it is important that they be kinematically consistent to very high accuracy. Small relative displacement errors can result in enormous local stresses.

An important class of problems may cause particular difficulties: these are the contact problems where load is applied to one structure via a second rigid or deformable body in local surface contact. Load is applied only where positive contact is maintained and slip and friction complicate the interface definition. Simplified contact problems will often be defined in displacement terms (eg a rigid pin loading a hole in a plate).

Some analysis systems will make explicit provision for contact problems in which case their instruction manuals should be followed with great care.

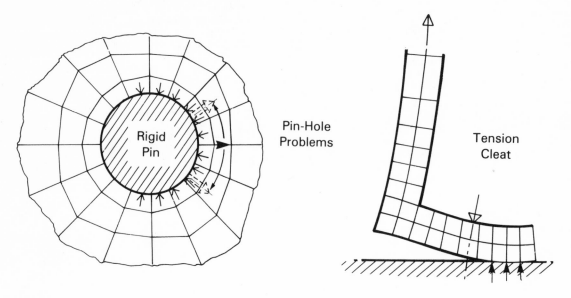

Rigid Pin

Pin-Hole Problems

Tension Cleat

**Contact Problems**

*Figure 3.3.3*

Loading via a rigid body with imposed displacements can lead to a fairly straightforward, iterative solution. Such analyses should only be attempted under the close supervision of a relatively expert analyst.

Before attempting any contact problem analysis ensure that the two structures in contact can be solved adequately for simple (eg constant pressure) boundary conditions.

### 3.3.4  *Masses and Inertias*

For maximum ease and accuracy in problem formulation, masses should be represented, element by element, as part of the element data. For most dynamic analyses this is not practical and it is common practice to use far fewer inertia variables than nodes in a structure.

The processes of determining equivalent inertia matrices are often complex and highly problem-dependent and cannot be covered here.

In controlling data preparation it is again necessary to ensure consistency especially in geometrical terms so that local moments and products of inertia are properly represented.

### 3.3.5  *General*

Loading actions are notoriously difficult to display graphically in formats suitable for data checking. It is therefore necessary to take particular care in their preparation and this is one area where independent checking and careful engineering supervision are strongly recommended.

## 3.4  CONSTRAINTS AND BOUNDARY CONDITIONS

This is probably the least understood and worst documented aspect of finite element analysis. Conditions other than single-point constraints and simple symmetry should not be tackled by inexperienced analysts without guidance either from a good and explicit manual or, preferably, an expert analyst.

### 3.4.1  *Single-point Constraints*

These cause few problems and there are usually only two main points to check:

- The constraints must be kinematically sufficient to remove all rigid body freedoms not expressly catered for in the analysis.

- The constraints should represent the physical problem.

**Checking should be against diagrams (difficult to generate by computer graphics) which should always accompany the problem specification.**

### 3.4.2  *Multi-point Constraints*

These may be used for many purposes such as coupling of nodes by rigid members, rectifying small geometric discrepancies and adjacent nodes representing locally offset supports and attachments etc.

**Constraint equations or displacement transformations, as required by the analysis system, must be formulated with extreme care and geometric consistency to the full analysis accuracy. It is better to truncate the nodal geometry data to ensure accurate transcription than to make errors in physically meaningless digits.**

Automatic equation generators are always to be preferred, in which explicit statements of geometry can be input and all derived terms obtained consistently.

If many similar constraint groups are used in a single analysis it is preferable to write a simple generation routine rather than set up separate matrices manually and run the risk of a geometric incompatibility which can destroy the accuracy of an analysis.

**If in any doubt always seek expert advice.**

$$
U \equiv \begin{bmatrix} u_i \\ v_i \\ u_j \\ v_j \end{bmatrix} = \begin{bmatrix} -d/2 & 0 \\ 0 & 1 \\ d/2 & 0 \\ 0 & 1 \end{bmatrix} \begin{bmatrix} \theta \\ V \end{bmatrix} \equiv T\bar{U}
$$

(a)  **Simple Flexure**

*Figure 3.4.2*  **Multi-point Constraint Transformations**

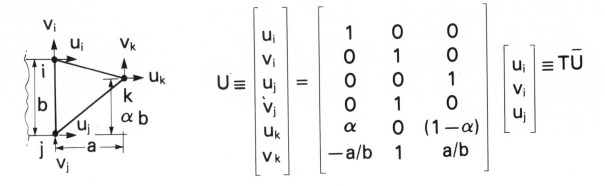

$$U \equiv \begin{bmatrix} u_i \\ v_i \\ u_j \\ v_j \\ u_k \\ v_k \end{bmatrix} = \begin{bmatrix} 1 & 0 & 0 \\ 0 & 1 & 0 \\ 0 & 0 & 1 \\ 0 & 1 & 0 \\ \alpha & 0 & (1-\alpha) \\ -a/b & 1 & a/b \end{bmatrix} \begin{bmatrix} u_i \\ v_i \\ u_j \end{bmatrix} \equiv T\bar{U}$$

(b) **Rigid Element**

$$U \equiv \begin{bmatrix} u_i \\ v_i \\ u_j \\ v_j \\ u_k \\ v_k \end{bmatrix} = \begin{bmatrix} 1 & 0 & 0 & 0 \\ 0 & 1 & 0 & 0 \\ \alpha & 0 & (1-\alpha) & 0 \\ 0 & \alpha & 0 & (1-\alpha) \\ 0 & 0 & 1 & 0 \\ 0 & 0 & 0 & 1 \end{bmatrix} \begin{bmatrix} u_i \\ v_i \\ u_k \\ v_k \end{bmatrix} \equiv T\bar{U}$$

(c) **Linear Interpolation**

*Figure 3.4.2* **Multi-Point Constraint Transformations**
*(contd.)*

### 3.4.3 *Hinges and Sliding Contact*

Structural releases are normally handled by the creation of pairs of initially coincident nodes in a structure. Elements are connected to one or other node of the pair and multi-point constraints are applied to connect those degrees of freedom which are mechanically coupled in the real structure (eg at a hinge, all translational freedoms are coupled but at least one rotational freedom is left uncoupled).

In many analysis systems, semi-automatic facilities are provided and it is only necessary to define the releases with care.

**It is especially necessary to check for correct element connections which should be shown on the element/grid plot recommended in Section 3.2.**

Sliding contact (ie one or more uncoupled translations) poses special problems because relative movement between points in contact introduces geometrical incompatibility unless special corrective devices such as multi-point constraints (iteratively related to deflections) are introduced (see Fig. 3.4.3).

**SLIDING CONNECTION**

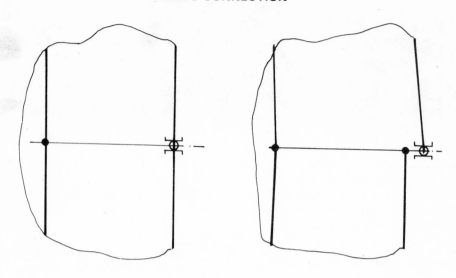

*Figure 3.4.3*   Geometric Offset under Load

If special sliding contact facilities are not provided and well documented this feature should not be introduced without expert advice.

### 3.4.4  Contact Problems

The special class of problems in which two separate surfaces are in contact only where positive pressure occurs between them is briefly dealt with in Section 3.3.

### 3.4.5  Force Boundary Conditions

Force boundary conditions are mainly introduced as loading actions as discussed in Section 3.3.

Some standard conditions (eg zero normal and shear stress at free edges) are built into element formulations, however

- Certain elements (especially those based on assumed-displacement functions) represent discontinuous applied forces rather badly, replacing local loads by statically equivalent distributed forces. Serious misrepresentation of loading should serve as an indicator of inadequate idealisation and may be corrected by better choice of elements, finer mesh subdivision or by the superposition of the results of a local analysis under self-equilibrating forces.

## 3.5 ADJACENT STRUCTURE AND SYMMETRY

### 3.5.1 *Interaction with Dissimilar Adjoining Structure*

Many analyses terminate at an interface with an adjoining structure which may or may not also be analysed by finite element methods.

If adjoining structure is passive (ie merely responds to actions from the subject structure as in an elastic foundation) it is only necessary to derive a boundary stiffness matrix for inclusion in the analysis. This is subject to the stringent requirements governing all special stiffnesses (Section 3.2), notably total geometric compatibility and force equilibrium.

If there is interaction in both directions it is necessary either to perform an interface analysis using substructure-type facilities or to assume a set of boundary forces/displacements (see later). In either case the analyst must establish total compatibility of loading cases and ensure that the combined structure is properly kinematically restrained.

**Wherever two adjoining structures interact, responsibility should be assigned to one analyst to manage and control the definition of the interface. This analyst should have overriding authority to ensure unique interface geometry and consistent loading conditions.**

### 3.5.2 *Symmetry and Repetition*

Simple 'reflection' symmetry and skew symmetry are readily handled in most finite element systems by simple and standard applications of single-point constraints at the axis or plane of symmetry. Likewise, multiple symmetries, and especially radial symmetry in cyclically repeating structures, may be handled by analysing individual segments with single-point constraints. Loading actions may need to be resolved into suitable components.

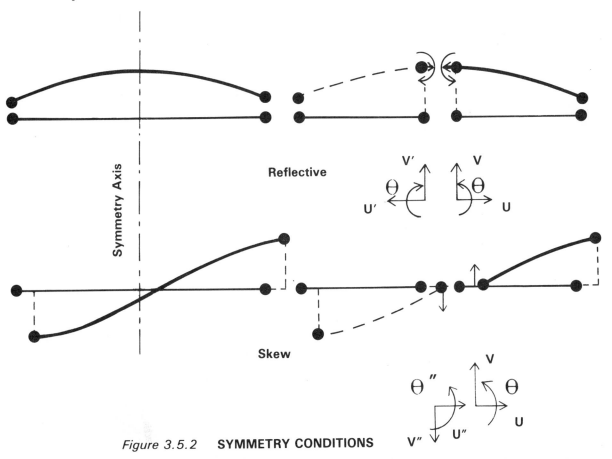

*Figure 3.5.2* **SYMMETRY CONDITIONS**

Few problems arise in conducting straightforward static analyses in these situations. However, special care is needed when combining symmetric with asymmetric substructures. Unless specific facilities are provided in the FE system, this requires full understanding of the use of the techniques of transformation of variables and particular attention to sign conventions.

**For analysts who have little or no experience in this field it is good practice to perform trial transformations using a greatly simplified problem with similar symmetry features, eg an extremely coarse mesh version of the same problem.**

Likewise the problem of (infinitely) repeated substructures, which is a common treatment for individual, locally loaded bays in a repetitive structure, requires simple transformations which relate displacements or forces at the two ends of an isolated bay, assuming that the next bay behaviour is identical or equal and opposite to the first.

Total axial symmetry is a different problem which enables a 3-dimensional axisymmetric structure to be analysed as a 2-dimensional radial slice. Special facilities should be provided for this case; if they do not exist, a wedge of structure may be analysed with multiple (cyclic) symmetry.

**Special care must be exercised in handling stability and dynamic problems in geometrically symmetric structures as there is no reason for buckling or vibration modes to show the same degree of symmetry as the geometry. Such analyses should not be attempted by inexpert analysts without either expert supervision, an explicit system manual or facilities for adequate research into the subject.**

### 3.5.3 *Assumed Interface Conditions*

If an interface occurs in a physically continuous region well removed from local loading actions or constraints it is often convenient to assume simplified conditions, such as conventional 'engineers' bending'.

In such a case it is necessary to be clear whether forces or displacements follow a prescribed pattern and to impose identical conditions to structure zones on both sides of the boundary.

Thus, for example, engineers' bending may be interpreted as

**either:** the imposition of rigid body displacements at the boundary (plane sections remain plane and undistorted)

**or:** the imposition of the pattern of stresses associated with classical bending/torsion theory under the above plane section conditions.

The two conditions are not identical and it may be prudent to try both separately. Any major discrepancy suggests that neither assumption is tenable and an interaction analysis is required.

## 4.1   SOLUTION METHODS

### 4.1.1   *Linear, Static Analysis*

Within any given system there will not normally be a choice of methods of solution. If a decision has to be taken between alternative systems, the following points may help selection:

- Elimination/pivotal condensation methods are often associated with good error checking and diagnostics.

- Frontal solutions are usually most economical in core utilisation.

- Factorisation methods are economical if analysis reruns are likely.

The principal selection criteria will normally be solution economics (accuracy:cost) and the quality of diagnostics/error warnings when the limits of solution capability are approached.

### 4.1.2   *Eigenvalue Analysis*

The choice of methods is highly dependent on the purpose of the analysis and the specific solution requirements. In all cases the analyst should possess some physical insight into the problem before selecting a method, so as to anticipate such occurrences as coincident values, unstable/bifurcation conditions and sensitivity to small non-linearities.

In straightforward eigenvalue problems three main types of requirement arise: recommendations are neither exhaustive nor definitive.

| Typical problem | Nature of solution | Suitable methods |
|---|---|---|
| Static stability<br>Aerolastic divergence<br>Critical speed | Lowest eigenvalue and corresponding vector | Inverse iteration<br>Lanczos/Q-R |
| Vibration modes for flutter analysis or modal response | Lowest set of (say) 6-10 eigenvalues and vectors | Jacobi:<br>sub-space iteration |
| Resonance/tuning | All values in a small range | Sturm sequence |

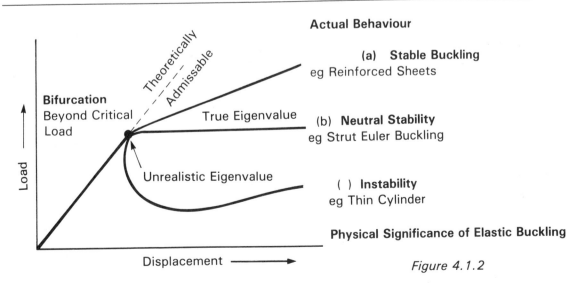

Figure 4.1.2

### 4.1.3 *Non-linear Statics*

Three main types of problem commonly arise, requiring very different solution treatment:

**(a)** Small deflection, non-linear coupling problems, typified by membrane/plate coupling via eccentricities and out of plane deformations. These are normally treated by the use of 'geometric stiffness' for which facilities are provided in most major analysis systems. Geometric stiffness formulation may lead to a stability (eigenvalue) solution or to a non-linear response situation which usually requires careful handling because displacements become indeterminate, or pass beyond the small displacement limits, as forces approach the critical (eigenvalue) levels.

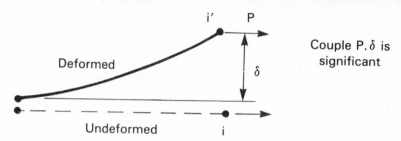

*Figure 4.1.3a* **Membrane-flexural Coupling**

**(b)** Large deflection, elastic analysis leads to greater complexities and is not satisfactorily handled by many commercial systems. Where facilities are provided it is essential that the analyst should clearly understand the physical problem, distinguishing, for example, follower forces (ie those whose directions change with structural deflections) from those with fixed directions. Complex instabilities may arise, not necessarily static in nature (eg the familiar hose-pipe effect). However, in many cases straightforward and useful solutions can be obtained, by careful incremental load analysis, modifying geometry at each step. Look for 'benchmark' or demonstration problem solutions appropriate to the problem in hand.

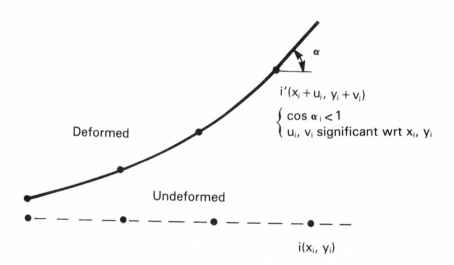

*Figure 4.1.3b* **Large Deflection/Elastic**

**(c)** Inelastic material behaviour in redundant structures leads to the most complex behaviour of all, insofar as solutions depend upon the history of loading from a known datum state as well as on current loading conditions. This is because permanent deformations accumulate in members previously stressed beyond the elastic limit. In practical structures (particularly those subject to thermal stresses) this may lead to one of two conditions over a long period of time.

- shakedown to a situation where inelastic deformations vary about a stable, typical condition

- incremental collapse situations where 'ratchet' mechanisms progressively increase the inelastic deformations until failure occurs.

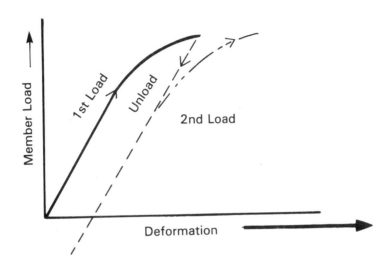

*Figure 4.1.3c* **Inelastic Material Behaviour**

No known general purpose systems provide adequate facilities for extensive analysis in this regime or for identifying criteria for transition from stable to unstable deformation. Small excursions into the inelastic regime for single 'overload cases can be handled by straightforward incremental loading and stiffness modification at each step. Beyond this, the analyst should seek expert advice, if not already thoroughly familiar with the problem, and should turn to specialist systems where available.

### 4.1.4 *Dynamic Analysis — Condensation and Modal Response*

Frequently a dynamic analysis is performed, using the same basic structural model as for statics, but requiring far fewer degrees of freedom than are inherent in that model. Most systems use the Guyan Reduction technique to condense the stiffness and inertia matrices. This relies on the selection of a relatively small number of master degrees of freedom, which must be chosen with care to match stiffnesses and significant masses. Some systems will provide selection facilities based on stiffness:mass ratio on the leading diagonal. It is possible, with poor selection, to generate spurious modes and introduce serious errors. Where proven automatic facilities are not provided, the analyst or supervisor must base selection on a sound physical appreciation of the problem.

Further condensation is often effected by the use of a limited number of natural (undamped) vibration modes using standard modal response techniques. The eigenvectors corresponding with the lowest natural frequencies are used as transformation matrices relating system deformations to modal displacement parameters. Automated facilities for modal response to prescribed loading and recovery of nodal displacements and stresses are normally provided in the major systems.

### 4.1.5  *Dynamic Analysis — Steady State*

Frequency domain analysis is common for steady-state periodic calculation, as encountered, for example, in fatigue life determination. If the periodic loading is complex it may be necessary to model with many harmonics; some systems will employ numerical (Fast Fourier Transform) methods to transform between time and frequency domains.

### 4.1.6  *Transient Response*

For rapid loading conditions, truncated modal response is inappropriate as the high frequency modes are significant. Several systems use direct integration marching procedures on the equations of motion for the full structure. These processes tend to be very expensive and depending upon whether explicit or implicit methods are used, the choice of time step may be critical as regards stability, as well as accuracy. This is a field of analysis for the specialist, where success depends upon the sensible choice of basic idealisation, substructuring and condensation as well as intelligent selection of dynamic variables and time steps matched to solution methods.

No transient dynamic analysis, of significance to structural safety, should be undertaken without expert involvement or assistance, irrespective of the degree of automation in the analysis system or the quality of documentation.

It will normally be necessary to turn to specialised systems to obtain reasonably economical solutions to rapid response and shock loading problems.

## 4.2   CHECKPOINT AND RESTART

Large finite element analyses can use a substantial computer resource and take a significant elapsed time to execute. The longer the analysis, also, the more prone it is to contain errors, despite intensive data vetting. It is therefore often advisable to break down the execution into easily manageable stages and establish *checkpoints* at which the results to date can be interrogated and blocks of intermediate data retained for subsequent use.

A long run may be interrupted either because of data errors or because of operational reasons (including running out of available time). It is usually possible to retrieve a large amount of work done to date but only if restart procedures are worked out and specified in advance.

For every major analysis an execution time estimate should be made and compared with the available new, or the recommended maximum, continuous running time on the available hardware.

**Where total estimated execution time approaches or exceeds the recommended limit, break the job down into stages by defining:**

- **checkpoints at which the analysis can be interrupted**

- **intermediate results required at each checkpoint**

- **data/results to be retained after each stage.**

**Where execution cost is a substantial fraction of the allowable budget ensure that restart procedures are defined which ensure recovery of the maximum feasible amount of intermediate data.**

Frequently, different types of analysis are required, using the same basic problem formulation, at different points in time. Checkpoint and restart facilities have their widest use in these circumstances, to identify data to be stored for subsequent analysis and the starting-up procedures making use of existing interim results. In some analysis systems the procedures are completely standardised and little or no analyst input is needed beyond a simple checkpoint instruction.

## 4.3    ILL-CONDITIONED ANALYSES

Finite element analysis often leads to ill-conditioning either in the final set of equations for solution (displacement methods) or in the equilibrium equations solved during matrix formulation (force methods). Apparent ill-conditioning may also arise when sufficient constraints have not been applied to a structure but truncation errors have made the resulting stiffness matrix appear non-singular.

It is possible for the order of magnitude of near-singularities to be similar for the two cases but for their effect on solution results to be markedly different.

Genuine ill-conditioning usually leads to loss of overall accuracy which can be detected by quite simple tests such as residual (force) checks. Spurious non-singularity may lead to quite large and obvious rigid body motions or local distortions at nodes where singularities are masked by truncation errors. However, the overall solution in residual (force) and internal stress/strain terms may be quite adequate in accuracy — this condition is thus not as serious as genuine ill-conditioning and is easier to track down.

Some common conditions which give rise to ill-conditioning and good practices for avoiding them are listed below.

| Condition | Method of avoidance |
|---|---|
| Adjacent node pairs with near identical displacements along their connecting line (eg nodes on each surface of a thin flexural structure). | Couple such nodes by rigid elements and eliminate one of the near identical pairs of degrees of freedom. |
| Connection of elements with vastly disparate stiffnesses at a common node (eg slender flexural member connected to membrane elements in-plane). | Modify idealisation to ensure comparable adjacent stiffness; *or* separate into distinct substructures. |
| Near-planar intersections of curved/twisted membrane elements or near collinear rod elements. | Modify idealisation, replacing membranes by flexural elements *or* use multi-point constraints to eliminate near-singularity by interpolation between adjacent degrees of freedom. |
| Very fine mesh analysis of flexible structures (absolute displacements many orders of magnitude larger than relative nodal displacements). | Breakdown substructures which localise the fine mesh zones. |

*NB:* If a very accurate solution procedure is available (eg double precision with 24-32 bit effective word lengths) none of the above conditions should cause trouble unless they are exaggerated to a pathological degree.

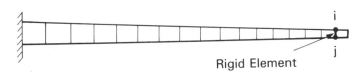

Figure 4.3a  **Adjacent node pairs on a slender spar or beam**

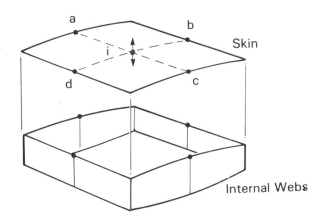

*Typical constraint equation:* $w_i = \tfrac{1}{4}(w_a + w_b + w_c + w_d)$

Figure 4.3b  **Near-planar intersection of curved sheet elements**

## 4.4  SOLUTION CHECKING

Two main kinds of solution checks (apart from visual inspection for major formulation errors) are recommended as good practice.

**(a)** Checks for numerical solution accuracy (effects of ill-conditioning, see Section 4.3).

**(b)** Checks for compatibility of solutions with assumed nature of analysis.

Most available systems provide for accuracy checking using one or more of the following methods.

### 4.4.1  *Accuracy Checks*

- Comparisons of residual nodal forces with those applied.

- Overall equilibrium (forces and, especially, moments).

- Nodal and element boundary force/displacement continuity (often only limited continuity is possible within the assumptions).

- Mathematical measures of accuracy determined as a by-product of the solution process, and special diagnostic aids.

Of these checks, the first three are physically meaningful and are best assessed by the analyst and/or supervisor. The fourth is often obscure to the user and is best interpreted by an expert unless explicit guidelines are given in the user manual. Diagnostic aids, in particular, can be highly problem dependent, but can be excellent facilities for the expert user.

Numerical accuracy can usually be improved by superimposing the solution to the same structural problem using residual forces as applied loads

$$\text{ie} \qquad \text{if } r_0 = K^{-1}R; \quad \Delta R = R - Kr_0 \quad \text{and} \quad r_1 = r_0 + K^{-1}\Delta R$$

Take note of all error and diagnostic messages and resolve their implications before accepting results.

A diagnostic and error check list should be provided to help inexperienced users.

### 4.4.2 *Compatibility with Nature of Analysis*

Some of the best analysis systems provide automatic checks to determine whether the results of an analysis lie outside the bounds implicit in the problem statement. More often it will be up to the analyst to inspect the solution for specific occurrences or up to his organisation to provide postprocessor facilities appropriate to the class of problems. Some occurences, such as convergence failure in dynamic and non-linear analyses, are so obvious as to need no special checking. Diagnosis of the cause and suitable correction procedures should be covered in reputable users' manuals. Some other possibilities, with recommended checking practices, are given below.

| Occurrence | Recommended practice |
|---|---|
| Displacements exceed the limits of conventional small displacement theory<br>— local geometry distortions<br>— overall displacement/slopes<br><br>in a linear static analysis. | Inspect displacement plots paying particular attention to 'shallow arch' snap-through type conditions, distortion of open sections in bending etc.<br>Overall conditions immediately apparent. |
| Materials exceed their elastic limit in a supposedly linear analysis. | Direct inspection of stress levels (obviously easily automated and often provided as a standard facility). |
| Local load offsets and eccentricities (especially in combined in-plane and flexural analyses of thin plates, beams and shells). | Should be accommodated as part of the basic problem formulation; if not, look for local normal displacements comparable with thickness or depth dimensions; where necessary, reformulate as a non-linear problem with geometric stiffness included. |

The most useful general checking tools are equilibrium checks and global/local displacement plots; looking for discontinuities in slopes as well as gaps and steps. Every analyst should become familiar with their use and supervisors should demand to see their results.

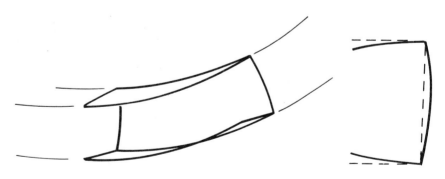

Section distortion significantly reduces flange stress

**Flexure of open section beam: non-linear effect**

*Figure 4.4.2*

## 4.5 SELECTION OF RESULTS

Finite element analyses are notorious for producing vast quantities of output which cannot be assimilated in total. This is particularly true when large numbers of loading cases and/or boundary conditions are analysed. To aid assimilation, various kinds of selection may be specified. Few basic analysis systems have any built-in selection features apart from prespecification of results and direct cut-off limits above (or below) which specific results should be quoted. More extensive selection features may be built into postprocessor facilities, which are often tailored to suit particular types of problem.

**Analysts should learn to ask for and use selection features rather than specify complete output as the latter are frequently dumped or filed without full appreciation of useful information. The needs of the job are paramount — ask for them.**

**However, complete output must always be available, on demand, to back up a first look based on selection.**

The following are some of the selection options which may be available, or suitable for specification.

| Selection criterion | Typical output |
|---|---|
| Maximum parameter value for every element. | Highest one or more values with respect to many loading cases, eg highest stresses or deflections. |
| Direct output values above and below prespecified limits. | For example critical principal stresses and elements/loading cases where they occur. |
| Maximum or minimum global parameter values | For example lowest natural frequency, largest deflection etc. |
| Maximum or minimum derived characteristics. | For example aerodynamic efficiency of a distorted wing; lowest structure weight. |
| Local parameter distribution in neighbourhood of maxima. | For example stresses near a point of stress concentration (for subsequent extrapolation/interpolation). |
| Local aberrations in parameter values. | For example local hot spots, surface distortions etc. |

## 4.6 PRESENTATION OF RESULTS

The preferred methods of presenting finite element results are:

**(a)** Graphical carpet or contour

- Distorted grid diagrams — static or animated.

- Plots on or related to the analysis grid.

- Response plots versus time, space or loading.

- Printed or coded results on analysis grids.

All the above should be available as hard copy prints (except, of course, animation) and the first three on suitable, interactive display screens.

**(b)** Numerical

- Selected tabulations (hard copy or screen).

- Numerical display with operator selection.

**Full listings should be available as an option on demand and should be discouraged as a primary form of presentation.**

Large amounts of time and storage space can be wasted by poring over, transcribing and filing away such listings. Direct output on microfilm provides a convenient storage and recovery medium.

### 4.6.1 *Recommendation for Graphical Presentation*

**Distorted grid diagrams are extremely useful for understanding structural behaviour and also as diagnostic aids when checking for and locating analysis errors. They should be produced as a standard output for any significant structural or dynamic analysis.**

Animation may be valuable for visualising transient response results where the output is vast or for conveying the significance of results to many users; it adds greatly to clarity, if not information content, but may be expensive in relation to its benefits.

Contour plots, particularly with coloured in-fill, are probably the most useful means of presenting variations in scalar quantities such as temperatures or absolute magnitudes of general quantities such as maximum principal stresses. To show vector quantities, special presentations such as arrows with scaled 'shaft' lengths may be preferred. These are particularly helpful when visualising stress patterns arround a stress raiser and illustrating load diffusion.

For all plots shown directly superposed on analysis grids, certain facilities are indispensable, including:

- ability to view from any angle

- hidden line removal and/or ability to view predetermined segments of the grid

- provision of sectioned views

- distinguishing lines by colour, intensity, hatching, pecking etc

- scaling and location of symbols and characters to avoid interference.

**Regular analysis users should make every effort to obtain adequate facilities of these kinds; this is usually the easiest case to present to management who are among the greatest beneficiaries in improved understanding, and acceptance of results.**

'One picture is worth a thousand words' can be taken literally as a conservative estimate of the useful information content of a high resolution graphics display, in computing word terms.

## 5.0 INTERPRETATION CHECKLIST

### 5.0.1 *Results Limitations*

Inherent limitations
— displacements
— stresses/strains
— others.

Manual or technical report references.

Analyst
— imposed limitations
— modelling
— load cases and boundary conditions
— incremental step sizes
— others.

### 5.0.2 *Engineering Assessment*

Name/position of assessor
Formal assessment of validity
Analyst/expert's justification
Agreed statement of conclusions.

### 5.0.3 *Interpolation, Extrapolation and Smoothing*

Continuous structure zones and appropriate results
Curve fitting formulae/facilities
Data points and interpolation/extrapolation points
Checks at prescribed stations
Boundary corrections and local analyses.

### 5.0.4 *Interfaces with Related Analyses*

Name of interface co-ordinator
Interface requirements definition and data
Formal supply of results
— name of supplier, date, standard
— special conditions or assumptions
— data location and supporting information.

### 5.0.5 *Real Structure Behaviour*

Routine corrections for section geometry etc
Transformations based on stress assumptions
Transformations based on displacements assumptions
Other transformations
Manual or report references.

## 5.1    RESULTS LIMITATIONS

Finite element analysis is essentially approximate and its results meaningful only within certain limits implicit in the basic assumptions. In general the analysis is numerically accurate (within limits discussed in Sections 4.3 and 4.4) as a solution of the formulated problem.

In a good analysis system, the manuals will make clear the limitations inherent in the use of particular elements and element combinations. Displacements will normally follow smooth curves and surfaces capable of easy interpolation and limited extrapolation. They can be subject to substantial overall errors as a result of element limitations.

Stress distributions within elements are often seriously misleading as they omit significant, locally self-equilibrating, stress systems, but the characteristic stress levels for whole elements are far more reliable.

Two main types of element formulation are commonly used; they give rise to quite different situations in interpreting results.

**(a)**  Displacement, or direct stiffness, formulation

Element displacement distributions are defined in terms of nodal displacement parameters; displacements and strains are compatible within the elements and at, and usually across, their boundaries. Equilibrium is established at node points in a limited number of degrees of freedom corresponding with the displacement parameters.

Stresses may be locally (and quite severely) distorted by neglecting self-equilibrating force systems needed to maintain the assumed displacement patterns. Thus internal stress distributions in the simpler elements are often misleading but the locally averaged stress outputs are reliable and can be successfully interpolated with some care. Regions of rapid load diffusions are the main area of concern; accurate solutions may require local mesh refinement or superposition of local approximate analysis.

**(b)**  Hybrid, or equilibrium (force) element formulations

Element stress distributions, in equilibrium internally and at the boundaries, are defined separately from the boundary displacements which are related to nodal displacements as above. Internal strains are derived from the stresses and not from boundary displacements. Strain compatibility with the boundary displacements and nodal force equivalence stress distributions are more meaningful than in displacement formulations but are not necessarily fully continuous across boundaries (equilibrium is established in terms of nodal loads rather than directly in terms of the stress parameters). Strains are not rigorously compatible between elements.

Displacement formulations always lead to over stiff representations of the structure. Hybrid formulations which make separate approximations to both stresses and displacements, may err in either direction and are sensitive to a good balance between the separate assumptions.

## 5.2 ENGINEERING ASSESSMENT

One of the commonest mistakes in applying any computing process is to assume that the output of a computing job has the validity inherent in the processing accuracy of the computer. This may lead, at best, to a complacency which may overlook errors or, at worst, to an inversion of logical reasoning to support an absurd result.

**No significant analysis result should be accepted without assessment to ensure its reasonableness. This assessment should, if possible, precede any complex processing of results.**

Engineering assessment always involves the inspection of individual or combined results which can be presented in a familiar form for ease of comparison with prior experience, with global quantities or with trends in adjacent regions.

Specifically, an assessor may look at:

- Smoothness and physical form of displacement patterns (exaggerated scale plots are helpful).

- Force/stress resultants (eg shear, BM and torque) either globally, at sections or in local subregions such as spars and ring frames.

- Constraint forces at supports, boundaries, junctions.

- Carpet or contour plots of stresses, strains, temperatures etc.

- Time or incremental loading histories of selected responses.

- Trajectories of principal stresses or other vector quantities.

It is not necessary for the assessor to have any specialist finite element knowledge in order to make valid criticism of results: general experience of the physical problem should suffice.

**Any query by a reputable assessor about the validity or meaningfulness of results must be answered by a credible physical explanation, using the information from the analysis. No justification based solely on esoteric knowledge of the system should ever be accepted.**

However, when unexpected results are confirmed by sound supporting evidence, a good assessor will add this to his store of general engineering knowledge.

## 5.3    INTERPOLATION, EXTRAPOLATION AND SMOOTHING

Finite element analysis, by definition, usually involves numerical approximation to continuous structure. Continuity is often physically specified only over certain regions; it is important to identify continuous structure regions and to specify the type of discontinuity expected at boundaries (eg rotation but not translation at a continuous hinge).

**Thus, before attempting any type of curve or surface fitting, divide the structure, and the appropriate output data into continuous zones representing the physical reality.**

Displacements are normally readily fitted by standard surface/curve-fitting methods.

**Stresses and strains are usually better fitted by surface/curve fitting through the point values stipulated at prescribed centres or integration points than by using internal stress/strain functions or by calculating values at convenient curve-fitting stations from these.**

This can be quite inconvenient unless the mesh was originally chosen with curve fitting in view (see Section 3.1). If a mesh is chosen for accuracy, or local refinement, which does not lend itself to curve fitting, significant errors may result. In some systems the problem is avoided by providing graphical output which is deliberately left discrete or unsmoothed so as to emphasise the approximate nature of results.

*NB:* There is no guarantee that interpolated/extrapolated stresses, anywhere other than at a natural section through stress definition points, will be in exact equilibrium with the global externally applied forces. This is a useful check on the validity of any approximate process and the best stress-fitting routines may include corrections for equilibrium at prescribed stations.

Extrapolation of stresses is only really meaningful at points away from local constraints or load inputs, which are often the very points at which stresses are most critical.

When using displacement-based element formulations, all free-edge stress distributions are suspect and it is sometimes helpful to use engineering knowledge and user-controlled corrections to impose known conditions not allowed for in element assumptions.

However, this must always be done as a correction to a curve fitted through actual analysis results. Attempts to fit a basic curve through boundary values determined separately from the analysis (however physically reasonable) are likely to lead to oscillations over several elements.

There is no adequate substitute for a local analysis (by finite element or other means) to determine the effects of the local self-equilibrating force system implicitly excluded by the finite element approximations. These local results may be superimposed on the basic analysis or fully incorporated by substructuring.

## 5.4 INTERFACES WITH RELATED ANALYSES

One analyst should be given overall responsibility for problems arising at any interface and for defining the requirements which one analysis imposes on another (see Section 1.5). The analyst supplying information at an interface must ensure that:

- Requirements of the related analysis are properly understood and the data supplied at the interface are rigorously derived and checked.

- Results are presented in the format, units and for the conditions prescribed by the co-ordinator.

- The interface data (especially geometry) have not changed in any way since setting up the analysis.

- Any special assumptions or limitations of concern to the neighbouring analysis are made known (eg emergence of significant non-linearity, symmetry conditions invoked etc).

Transfer of data from one analysis to another should be formal and accompanied by:

- the name of the supplier and date of supply

- information defining the standard of the structure and boundary conditions

- reference to the requirement or specification against which data are delivered

- identification of the data transfer medium and data location

- cost data (as required) on the analysis performed and any extensions or re-runs.

Sub-structure interface data in computer files should, if possible, be protected by security routines giving read-only access to all users except the analyst with overall responsibility.

## 5.5    REAL STRUCTURE BEHAVIOUR

The process of mesh selection (Section 3.1) and element idealisation (Section 3.2) replace real structure by an idealised model for analysis purposes.

Idealisation involves a number of formal or implicit operations to determine structural equivalence which must be inverted or reversed when interpreting analysis results. Where there is a one-to-one equivalence between idealised and real members (eg when making small corrections for curvature or finite depth of continuous sheet elements) a reverse transformation is readily identified and will provide a simple results correction.

Very often this is not the case, eg where discrete members have been lumped together or a group of fasteners represented by a single spring stiffness. In this situation there is no unique inverse and it is necessary to devise a transformation which is at least fully consistent with that used in idealisation. The two commonest conditions involve equivalence in terms of stress resultants assuming either a prescribed stress pattern or local displacements as in the following examples.

*Example A*

Several stiffeners are lumped into a single idealised member of equal total area and second moment of area about a prescribed axis.

This condition assumed simplified 'engineers' bending' about a known axis and the same condition can be assumed in transforming stresses. Stresses at two/three adjacent stations can be used to estimate a linear section variation and stresses at real stations calculated therefrom.

*Example B*

A multi-layer laminate is represented by an equivalent plate stiffness matrix.

As in example A the existence of an equivalent plate stiffness implies simplified membrane/tension behaviour and the simplifying plate conditions can be imposed using `displacements or rotations` from the analysis to compute layer deformations and stresses.

In all cases, particular note must be made of the position(s) within an element where stresses are defined; this is particularly important near free edges where it may be necessary to extrapolate over a portion of an element to estimate local stress peaks.

## 6.1   RECORDING THE ANALYSIS

Every significant analysis should be well documented making as much use as possible of automatic printout of actual data submitted and derived. Ideally the majority of formal documentation should be self-generated as a normal by-product of data entry and results presentation. Provision of interactive facilities for this purpose is strongly recommended.

Formal documentation should include:

- Problem specification, eg using the pro forma of Section 1.0.

- Supporting diagrams illustrating

  — the real structure geometry, loadings and boundary conditions

  — the idealised structure mesh and local details

  — interfaces with neighbouring structures

  — required results presentation.

- Key input data including

  — basic geometry data or data source

  — mesh plots showing element locations

  — detailed definition of boundary conditions and constraints

  — definition of all loading cases, temperature conditions etc

  — key drawing references including issues/standards

  — idealisation data, procedures and key parameters

  — materials and environmental data.

- Selected output data as defined in the specification and normally including:

  — displaced structure plots

  — selected stress/strain tabulations

  — carpet or contour plots

  — section plots as defined

  — incremental histories for selected results

  — data for use in associated analyses (eg boundary stiffness, vibration modes strain energy densities etc).

## 6.2    REPORTING THE FINDINGS

Many analyses are conducted as part of routine design and the output is naturally used as the input to a whole series of follow-on calculations. In these cases the findings may need no special comment beyond what is rightly included in the output documentation: the rest of this section does not apply.

In many other instances the analysis is part of an investigation in its own right, eg the determination of structural instability or post-buckling behaviour, study of deformations and clearances, explanation of experimental findings etc. In such cases the job is not complete until an interpretive report is produced. This is a step often neglected by stress analysts who tend to consider their job complete when results are published.

The analyst and supervisor are usually the best people to interpret results for others and it is good practice to conclude any exploratory analysis with a brief report containing the following:

- Purpose of the investigation.

- Outline of the model and problem representation.

- Summary of principal results.

- Discussion of results especially physical significance and accuracy limits.

- Key for locating results and data, plus reference to the version/release number of the program used.

- Conclusions and recommendations.

## 7.0   EXPECTATIONS OF AN ANALYSIS SYSTEM

This section summarises some of the features which a user should expect to find in a finite element system offered for general use in structural/mechanical design. It is intended as a guide, not as a specification of requirements.

Many of the recommendations and injuctions are to be found elsewhere in the text but are not cross-referenced. The recommendations are in four sections:

Documentation

Data preparation, verification and preprocessing

Analysis facilities

Results presentation, selection and postprocessing.

7.1.2  A good system will be further supported by any or all of the following:

(a)  An applications manual* describing the use of the system in solving typical problems.

(b)  A validation/demonstrating manual* comprising

- examples to demonstrate correct operation of an installed system

- examples to demonstrate the accuracy of solutions obtainable over the useful range

- solutions to standard benchmark problems with relevant statistics.

(c)  A training handbook (or on-line facility) for systematic induction and training of users and operators.

(d)  A program manual* giving logical details of all fundamental operations and procedures.

(e)  A system development plan plus documentation on user liaison, support and feedback services.

(f)  Supporting system manuals, eg for mesh generation and results presentation systems.

---

*Note: It is not necessary that manuals be physically separate, only that the contents be available in standard documentation.

## 7.1    ANALYSIS SYSTEM DOCUMENTATION

7.1.1    Apart from experimental in-house programs where there will be on-site expertise, all systems to be used for design/verification purposes must be supported by:

a        A user manual* describing, at least:

•        the capabilities of the system, in user terms

•        all data entry and output formats

•        the solution facilities available

•        generation of instructions for execution and control.

b        A theoretical manual* describing, at least:

•        the theoretical basis for the elements used

•        the theoretical basis for the solution procedures

•        the theoretical basis for all standard operations and facilities provided

•        the principal limitations on element geometry, mesh size, loading conditions, numerical parameters in solutions etc

•        evidence validating the system within its recommended range of uses

and when the system is to be operated in house:

c        A systems manual* describing, at least:

•        the computer hardware configuration(s) required

•        the operating system/control software

•        data entry, job execution, job control and output instructions

•        system operational diagnostic procedures

•        data and execution error messages and correction procedure.

---

*Note: It is not necessary that manuals be physically separate, only that the contents be available in standard documentation.

## 7.2    DATA PREPARATION, VERIFICATION AND PREPROCESSING

7.2.1   Every general purpose analysis system must provide standard formats for input of 'raw data' including:

- mesh geometry (nodal co-ordinates)

- element data

- loading and environmental data

- inertia data

- constraint data.

Every system should provide some degree of data vetting on entry, comprising, at least:

- consistency checks for element types/topology

- mesh continuity, grid plotting

- kinematic constraint/singularities.

7.2.2   The user may reaonably expect, in addition:

- further diagnostic aids to data validation

- automatic constraint generators

- mesh generation aids

- load case generation aids

- substructure boundary definition aids

- visualisation of loading and section property resultants

- aids to node numbering/renumbering.

7.2.3 In addition to facilities provided as part of the basic analysis suite the user may look for preprocessor systems which generate data suitable for direct entry into the system. These may include:

- automatic mesh generation linked to CAD geometry system and including substructuring and node numbering

- extensive (interactive) graphical display featuring sections, angled views, element visualisation, property plots, contours etc.

- automatic load generators (eg converting pressures to nodal loads and computing balancing inertia forces)

- inertia matrix generators and/or interface to mass analysis system

- automated element idealisation routines, especially for multi-layer laminates and other composite sltructures.

## 7.3    ANALYSIS FACILITIES

7.3.1   Every analysis system must provide basic solution procedures for linear, elastic, static analysis. This must provide for prescribed loadings, and kinematic constraints and must generate overall displacements and element stresses.,

7.3.2   Every general purpose system should provide, in addition to the above:

- solutions for prescribed tememperature distributions

- determination of structural flexibilities

- eigenvalue (critical load, frequency, speed) analysis

- modal response dynamic analysis

- geometric stiffness coupling for elastic stability analysis

- substructure analysis and stress recovery

- error indentification and diagnostic facilities

- numerical conditioning checks.

7.3.3   The best, or the more specialised, systems may provide any or all of the following:

- large deflection elastic analysis

- non-linear, inelastic analysis

- steady state and transient dynamic analysis

- impulsive and shock wave analysis

- power spectral analysis

- heat flow analysis

- interface with boundary integral methods

- infinitely recursive subdivision techniques

- generalised differential equation solution

- alternative solution routines, biased towards low cost, accuracy, computer size or other criteria

- interactive help facilities

- specialised outputs, eg response derivatives with respect to structural sizes (for optimisation).

## 7.4 RESULTS, PRESENTATION, SELECTION AND POSTPROCESSING

7.4.1 Every general purpose analysis system must provide the facility to output the following:

- tabulation of global displacements, element stresses and external constraint forces

- plots of deformed structure

- error messages and warnings, whether overridden or not.

7.4.2 A good system should provide, in addition to the above:

- facilities to select output by structural zone, predetermined value limits or comparative criteria (eg maximum principal stresses)

- element nodal forces or boundary distributions where required

- internal (multi-point) constraint forces

- substructure boundary forces and/or displacements

- precise location, as well as magnitude, of all stress ouptputs

- deflection/stress interpolation and local extrapolation facilities

- stress/load intensity plots on a structural grid, including, contour plots and section plots

- temperature tabulations and plots on structural grids

- response plots versus time, space or load level

- derived load resultants (eg shear force, BM) at predefined stations.

7.4.3 Separate postprocessor facilities may provide, in addition to some of the above:

- (colour) plots with arbitrary viewpoints, sectioning, windowing, highlighting, shading etc

- animated displays, especially of dynamic response

- specialised outputs (eg energy densities) for input to related routines (optimisation)

- conversion of results to the real structure; detail stressing (eg bolt groups, plate stability etc).

# NAFEMS GUIDELINES TO FINITE ELEMENT PRACTICE    Addendum

## Glossary of Terms

This glossary includes terms used generally or casually throughout the text, which are outside the normal usage in structural/mechanical engineering.

It does not necessarily include:
- definitions of terms which are explained in the text in the only places where they occur.
- terminology used in specialised discussion, whose meaning is well understood within the field.
- normal English usage of common words such as "element", when such usage should be evident from the context.

| | |
|---|---|
| **Acceptance criteria** | Conditions laid down by a prospective recipient of information which are to be met by the supplier. |
| **Active adjoining structure** | Structure which has a common boundary with that being analysed and which is subject to loading in addition to that via the interface. |
| **Analysis, Finite element** | *see* **Finite element analysis.** |
| **Analysis Grid** | *see* **Grid.** |
| **Analysis, Impact** | *see* **Impact analysis.** |
| **Analysis, Local** | *see* **Local analysis.** |
| **Analysis Specification** | A formal statement of a particular problem to be solved and the analyst's requirements for its representation, solution and presentation. |
| **Analysis, Thermal** | *see* **Thermal analysis.** |
| **Analyst, Expert** | *see* **Section 0.5.** |
| **Application software** | Computer programs and operating systems for executing problem-solving tasks. |
| **Automatic generation (of data, meshes etc.)** | Any means whereby computer-aids are used to produce input data for a computer analysis from simplified instructions given by the analyst. |
| **Axes** | *see* **Principal axes, Transformation of axes.** |
| **Axial symmetry** | A property of any body of revolutions in which all radial sections are identical. |
| **Axisymmetric** | Possessing axial symmetry. |
| **Benchmark tests** | Fully specified standard problems used for evaluating the performance of (finite element analysis) systems. |
| **Bifurcation** | A sudden change (usually following contained buckling) in the load/deformation characteristics of a structure (*see* **Section 4.1**). |
| **Boundary conditions** | Loading and deformation conditions imposed at structure nodes and implied along grid boundaries, including all external constraints. |
| **Boundary continuity (Section 3.0)** | The condition whereby adjacent elements in a structure are in continuous contact and remain so during structure deformation. |
| **Buckling** | A condition in which a structure deforms out of the plane of loading at some critical load level, usually into an approximately harmonic wave pattern. |
| **Carpet plot** | A plot in which a function of two or more variables is depicted as a surface by lines at discrete parameter values. |
| **Checkpoints** | Pre-planned break points in the execution of an analysis at which specified data are stored for subsequent restarting. |
| **Coincident nodes** | Analysis grid nodes with identical co-ordinates but attached to separate elements. |
| **Compatibility** | The Conditions whereby:<br>(a) different things (such as types of element) are suitable for use in conjunction (especially with common boundaries).<br>(b) deformations are continuous and strains are obtained from their derivatives. |
| **Composite** | A form of construction or material which is built up from several macroscopic constitutients with different mechanical properties; specifically, a laminated form of construction wherein adjacent layers are similar orthotropic laminae with different orientations. |

| | |
|---|---|
| **Connectivity** | The condition of connection between adjacent elements in a structure; the relationship between the nodes of a mesh and those of individual elements. |
| **Consistency** | The·condition whereby different things satisfy a common set of assumptions or conditions. |
| **Constraints** | Any limitations placed upon the deformations of a structure which are not implicitly contained within the description of its elements. |
| **Consultant, Expert** | *see* **Section 0.5.** |
| **Contact problems** | A class of problems in which deformable bodies are in contact over a region which varies according to the loading conditions, i.e. they are connected only by physical (pressure) contact. |
| **Continuity (mesh)** | Refers specifically to avoiding unintentional terminations of grid lines along element boundaries which cannot accommodate them. |
| **Conventional stiffness (Section 1.6)** | Specifically refers to stiffness matrices expressed in terms of all relevant degrees of freedom (implicitly including rigid body motions)<br>*cf* **Natural stiffness.** |
| **Cyclic symmetry** | A property of a body comprising identical segments arranged sequentially around an axis. |
| **Degrees of freedom** | The total set of displacement variables which are needed to describe the deformation of a point, an element or structure in a discrete variable representation; a measure of the size of an analysis.<br>(*see* **Spurious degrees of freedom**). |
| **Determinate boundary conditions** | Boundary conditions which can be fully specified prior to analysis. |
| **Deterministic loading** | Loading conditions specified as one or more sets of absolute values of loading parameters<br>*cf* **Stochastic loading.** |
| **Diagnostic(s)** | Information about errors in executing analyses and aids to identification of their causes. |
| **Direct (dynamic) response** | Response computed directly in terms of all relevant degrees of freedom<br>*cf* **Modal response.** |
| **Discrete parameter** | General description of the approximate treatment of continuous phenomena in terms of a finite number of discrete variables. |
| **Displacement formulation (of element stiffness)** | A method of finite element stiffness determination based mainly on assumed displacement functions within and between elements (*see* **Section 5.1**)<br>*cf* **Hybrid formulation.** |
| **Displacement transformation** | A linear relationship between two sets of displacement variables, i.e. expressing one set as a linear combination of the other. |
| **Effective material/structure** | Material or structure which is assumed to contribute significantly to overall structural behaviour: a concept relevent to classical stress analysis but usually inappropriate in finite element analysis. |
| **Eigenvalue** | A singular or critical value of a parameter at which a non-trivial solution of a problem can exist; in structural analysis, usually a natural frequency or buckling load parameter.<br>(mathematically) A root of the characteristic equation of the matrix $(A-\lambda B)$. |
| **Eigenvector** | A vector of state variables (e.g. displacements) associated with the eigenvalue and determinate in relative but not absolute magnitude;<br>The vector $U_i$ such that $\left[A-\lambda_i B\right] U_i = 0$<br>In structural analysis, a vibration or buckling mode. |
| **Element, Finite** | *see* **Finite element.** |
| **Element, Special** | *see* **Special element.** |
| **Element type** | A designation given to the set of elements characterised by common topology, material and section parameters and internal behaviour assumptions. |
| **Elimination** | The process of solving simultaneous equations by successively evaluating one or more variables in terms of the remainder; systematic operations on matrices which perform the equivalent function. |
| **Energy density** | The ratio of energy (usually elastic strain energy) stored in an element to its volume; a powerful measure of structural effectiveness of different elements. |

| | |
|---|---|
| **Expert Analyst, Consultant, Supervisor** | *see* **Section 0.5.** |
| **Explicit equations** | Equations supplied directly as sets of coefficients, already evaluated. |
| **External constraint** | Any constraint imposed on the external boundary of a structure, usually as part of the assumed structural support. |
| **Faceted shell element** | A flat or nearly-flat element with linear edges, used to approximate to a segment of a curved shell. |
| **Facilities** | The usable set of computing hardware, peripherals, software and documentation available to the analyst. |
| **Factorisation** | The breaking down of a matrix into a product of two or more simpler matrices to aid inversion or repetitive solution. |
| **Features, Special structural** | *see* **Special structure features.** |
| **Features, Sub-scale** | *see* **Sub-scale features.** |
| **Finite** ⎰ deflection ⎱ deformation ⎱ displacement | A regime in which displacements are large enough to modify the gemoetry significantly, especially as regards to the impact of external loads<br>    *cf* **small deflection.** |
| **Finite element** | The smallest significant sub division of an idealised structure; a class or type of such structural units. |
| **Finite element analysis** (*see* **Section 0.2**) | The analysis of continuous bodies or media as assemblages of discrete members or elements. |
| **Finite element system** | A set of computer programs with supporting theory and documentation. |
| **Finite strain** | A regime in which strains are geometrically significant within individual elements (normally $> > 1\%$). |
| **Fixed forces** | Forces whose directions do not change as a result of (finite) structural deformation. |
| **Flexibility matrix** | A matrix which relates displacements to the corresponding forces which produce them; a matrix of structural influence coefficients. |
| **Flexural elements** | A class of thin rod, plate and shell elements described solely in terms of bending, twisting and normal shearing behaviour<br>    *cf* **membrane elements.** |
| **Flexural properties** | Bending, twisting and normal shearing properties of the cross sections of flexural elements. |
| **Follower forces** | Forces whose directions change, following the shape of the structure during finite deformation. |
| **Force formulation**<br>(of element forces)<br><br>(of structural analysis) | Any method of finite elements behaviour description which is based upon an assumed stress pattern in equilibrium with boundary and body forces.<br>Analysis in terms of forces as primary variables. |
| **Formulation** ⎰ Displacement ⎱ Force | *see* **Displacement formulation.**<br>*see* **Force formulation.** |
| **Foundations** | The assumed fixed mounting or support points for a structure. |
| **Frontal solution methods** | Methods for solving linear equations in which all calculations progress through the matrices by one column (front) at a time. |
| **Generalised displacements** | Sets of displacements (usually relative displacements of two or more points) which can be described by a single parameter. |
| **Generalised forces** | Sets of forces and/or distributed loadings which can be defined by a single parameter; usually self equilibrating or statically equivalent force groups. |
| **Generation, mesh** | *see* **Mesh generation.** |
| **Geometric stiffness** | A stiffness (matrix) which defines the flexural forces which result from the (finite) displacement of initially in-plane forces; it contains force as a linear factor (e.g. bending moment versus lateral displacement in a compressed strut). |
| **Global** ⎰ behaviour ⎱ deflections/ ⎱ displacements ⎱ properties | The behaviour, response or properties of a structure viewed as a whole and related to a single set of reference axes<br>    *cf* **local behaviour etc.** |
| **Grid (Analysis)** | The network of lines which defines the idealised geometry of structure and the boundaries of its finite elements. |

| | |
|---|---|
| **Hinges (specific usage)** | Attachments between coincident pairs of analysis grid nodes which permit rotation about at least one axis but no translation. |
| **Hybrid formulation (of element stiffness)** | A method of stiffness derivation in which force and displacement patterns are separately defined in terms of boundary parameters and are matched by energy minimisation. |
| **Idealisation** | The process of representing real, continuous structure by an equivalent, finite element model. |
| **Idealised (model) structure** | The conceptual structure which is described by the finite element analysis data and which is the analyst's representation of the real structure. |
| **Ill-conditioning** | A property (of a matrix), related to the choice of problem variables, which causes abnormal loss of accuracy during numerical solution. |
| **Impact analysis** | Analysis under impulsive loading. |
| **Indeterminate boundary conditions** | Conditions of contact between adjacent bodies which change under load and hence cannot be specified fully in advance. |
| **Inertia matrix** | A matrix, comprising masses and first and second moments of inertia, defining the inertia properties of a body in all relevant degrees of freedom. |
| **Interaction (structural)** | The mutual influence of one structure upon another; in finite element analysis the coupling of forces and displacements across a common boundary between two separately analysed structures. |
| **Interface (specific usage)** | The common boundary between separate structures. |
| **Invariance (of stiffness matrices)** | The independence of a stiffness matrix expressed in any one co-ordinate system with the choice of axes for stiffness derivation. |
| **Isostatics** | Lines of constant (maximum principal) stress. |
| **Kinematic** boundary conditions constraints etc. | Conditions expressed solely in terms of limitations on displacement (e.g. rigid support). |
| **Kinematic modes** | Combinations of displacements (of an element), which result in no apparent forces; a pathological occurrence in some poorly formulated element types. |
| **Kinematically sufficient** | Constraints which remove all rigid body degrees of freedom. |
| **Laminated composite** | A form of plate or shell construction built up of non-homogeneous layers with differing properties; especially orthotropic laminae with different orientations. |
| **Large** deflections deformations displacements | *see* **Finite deflections etc.** |
| **Layer orientation** | The principal direction of an orthotropic layer in a laminated composite relative to a specified datum. |
| **Lay-up (of laminated composite)** | The sequence of layer orientations and thicknesses. |
| **Loading case** | A complete set of forces and associated boundary conditions for which a solution is required. |
| **Local analysis (specific usage)** | A supplementary analysis (usually under self-equilibrating forces and confined to a single element) used to correct for the restrictive assumptions of the element formulation. |
| **Local** behaviour deflections displacements properties etc. | Behaviour expressed in relation to a single element in a structure or its immediate vicinity, often in element axes. |
| **Matrix** Flexibility Inertia Stiffness Symmetric | *see* **Flexibility.** *see* **Inertia.** *see* **Stiffness.** *see* **Symmetry.** |
| **Membrane elements** | A rod, plate or shell element which represents only the in-plane stiffness properties, assumed uncoupled from flexure *cf* **flexural element.** |
| **Mesh** | *see* **Grid.** |

| | |
|---|---|
| **Mesh generation** | The process of producing the explicit node, line, or surface definition data from some simplified instructions and reference geometry, often using interactive graphics. |
| **Method, Solution** | *see* **Solution method.** |
| **Modal** { analysis freedoms response } | Problem formulation (or its variables) in terms of a number of generalised displacements, usually a finite number of normal vibration or buckling modes of structure. |
| **Mode** | A pattern or set of relative displacements which, together with an amplitude parameter, defines a deformed shape. |
| **Model** | The idealised structure and its loading environment. |
| **Modelling** | The process of generating a model as an approximate representation of a real problem. |
| **Natural** { degrees of freedom stiffness } | A set of generalised, independent displacements which represents structural distortions, and excludes all rigid body motions; stiffness expressed in such terms<br>    *cf* **conventional stiffness.** |
| **Node(s)** | The junction and definition points in a structural grid. |
| **Node sequencing** | Ordering of the node reference numbers for convenience or efficiency in solution. |
| **Offsets** | Local misalignments of loadings or axes which may introduce significant secondary loadings. |
| **Optimisation** | Any process of recalculation of design parameters to improve structural performance. |
| **Orthotropic (material)** | Possessing unequal, though symmetric properties in two perpendicular directions (principal axes). |
| **Passive adjoining structure** | Structure which has a common boundary with that being analysed but is unloaded except via the interface. |
| **Patch test** | A test applied to a small group of elements to demonstrate their performance under uniform strain. |
| **Piece-wise linear** | Describes a load-deformation relationship represented by a sequence of two or more straight lines. |
| **Post-buckling** | The condition in which a structure can continue to support load above its first critical (buckling) load. |
| **Post-processor** | A computer system for manipulating and/or displaying the results of finite element analysis. |
| **Pre-processor** | A computer system for helping to prepare input data for finite element analysis. |
| **Primary structure** | Structure judged to be the most significant for the transmission of specified loads; a concept of little direct relevance to finite element analysis. |
| **Principal axes (general)** | Sets of perpendicular axes relative to which section or material properties are symmetrical (no cross-products or coupling terms). |
| **Principal (leading) diagonal (of a matrix)** | The set of elements of a square matrix which are located diagonally from top L to bottom R. |
| **Quasi-linear** | Sufficiently near to linear to be satisfactorily treated as such. |
| **Quasi-static** | Varying load conditions which may be treated as static (the normal situation with slowly fluctuating loads). |
| **Radial symmetry** | Repeated symmetry about radial sections in a body of revolution<br>    (*see* **cyclic symmetry**). |
| **Real structure** | The actual structure to be analysed as distinct from its mathematical or numerical counterpart. |
| **Redundant data** | Measured data which are more than sufficient to define an independent set of quantities; therefore data which are potentially in conflict through numerical or experimental errors. |
| **Reflection symmetry** | The condition whereby an object can be represented as two halves, one the mirror image of the other. |
| **Releases** | Incomplete couplings between the displacements of elements meeting at a commone node (*see* **hinges and sliders**). |

| | |
|---|---|
| **Repetition (of identical structure)** | A condition analogous to symmetry whereby adjacent regions of a structure are identical and the connection conditions are the same for all adjoining pairs. |
| **Residual nodal forces** | Forces which result from numerical inaccuracies and given by Applied load — (Stiffness × Displacement) at the nodes; a useful measure of accuracy in displacement-based analysis. |
| **Secondary structure** | Structure judged to be unimportant in transmitting primary loads; a concept of little direct relevance to finite element analysis. |
| **Single point constraints** | Specified (usually zero) displacements applied to individual nodes. |
| **Singularity elements** | Finite elements whose formulation includes mathematical singularities, especially for representing abrupt discontinuities such as cracks. |
| **Skew symmetry** | A condition whereby loads and displacement on each side of a plane of symmetry are equal but opposite in sign to a mirror image. **(Note:** every load system on a symmetric structure can be resolved into symmetric and skew-symmetric components). |
| **Sliders** | Releases which permit translation, but not rotation, between initially coincident nodes. |
| **Solution methods** | The analytical or numerical algorithms used within particular finite element programs. |
| **Special features** | Structural features (in a real structure) which do not form a part of a regular or continuous pattern but which need to be represented in finite element analysis (e.g. joints, local holes etc.). |
| **Special elements** | Element types introduced by the analyst to supplement those available in the standard library; often introduced as pre-calculated stiffness matrices. |
| **Specification, Analysis** | *see* **Analysis specification.** |
| **Spurious degrees of freedom** | Degrees of freedom which are present in a stiffness matrix but have no stiffness terms associated with them; they must be eliminated. |
| **State variables** | Variables which define the current state of stress or strain throughout a structure. |
| **Stiffness matrix** | Any array of coefficients which linearly relate forces to their corresponding displacements; the inverse of a flexibility matrix. |
| **Stochastic (variables)** | Quantities which are continually varying in time and are described only in terms of power spectral densities *cf* **deterministic.** |
| **Strains** | *see* **Thermal strains.** |
| **Structure** { **Real / Idealised** | *see* **Real structure.** <br> *see* **Idealised structure, model.** |
| **Sub-scale features** | Features of a real structure which are too small to be represented economically by the basic mesh but whose influence on element properties should be included. |
| **Sub-structure** | Groups of structural elements which are analysed independently and subsequently connected to other elements or sub-structures via interaction or 'super-structure' analysis. |
| **Supervisor, Expert** | *see* **Section 0.5.** |
| **Supports** | Points/degrees of freedom which are kinematically constrained and where external loads are reacted. |
| **Symmetry (structural)** | A condition which enables an object to be fully represented by mirror images about one or more planes *see* **axial-, cyclic-, radial and skew symmetry.** |
| **Symmetry (matrix)** | Describes a special form of square matrix in which rows and columns are interchangeable. |
| **System, Finite element** | *see* **Finite element system.** |
| **Thermal analysis** | Analysis of the transmission of heat through structures and related media. |
| **Thermal strains** | Structural strains which result from the restraint of free thermal expansion/contraction. |
| **Thermo-structural analysis** | Analysis in which the effects of thermal transmission, distortion and mechanical loading are combined. |
| **Topology** | The conceptual sub division of space by lines and surfaces (recognising connection, branching, inside/outside etc. without actual geometry). |
| **Truncation** | Cutting short, especially of strings of numbers for numerical computation. |
| **Validation** | Demonstration of the accuracy and reliability of a sytem or a set of results. |
| **Wave front solution** | A transient dynamic solution representing the propagation of a disturbance in space. |